THE SCHOOL

TO THE
BASEBALL
FIELD

THE POND

THE CHURCH

DONNA

for DAVID
from
al Guinness

Nov 7
1974

DON and DONNA GO TO BAT

By Al Perkins
Illustrated by
B TOBEY—

BEGINNER BOOKS A Division of Random House, Inc.

Don and Donna were twins.

Don was a boy.

Donna was a girl.

Each was exactly as tall as the other.

Their voices sounded exactly alike.

They both had blue eyes, red hair, and . . .

. . . they each had the same number of
freckles on their faces,
23 to be exact.
Don wore boys' clothes
and had short hair.
Donna wore girls' clothes
and had long hair.
That is how you could tell them apart.

Don loved baseball.

Day after day,

he would go outside the house

and throw his ball up against the wall.

He liked to pretend
he was a batter who
had made a hit.
Then he would run and
slide into base.

On Don's birthday,

his twin sister, Donna, gave him a

wonderful present.

She gave him a real baseball suit,

a ball, a bat, a glove, and a cap.

Don was so happy
he took his birthday presents
to bed with him
every night.

He always dreamed he was playing
on a real baseball team.

Like many girls, Donna did not know
how to play baseball.
So Don showed her
how to play.

Donna already could run
as fast as her brother.

Don showed her how to throw a ball
the way a boy throws it.

He showed her how
to slide into base.

He showed her how
to hold the bat . . .

. . . and how to
stand at the
plate.

Donna didn't like to bat.
When her brother
threw the ball
at her . . .

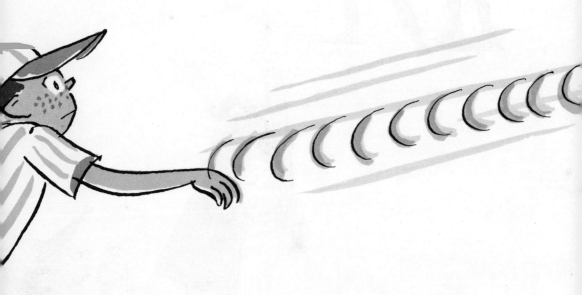

. . . she was frightened
and her knees shook.

She shut her eyes tight.
Then she swung the bat
at the ball.

Usually she missed it.

But she liked to pitch
the ball
to Don . . .

and run after it

16

when he hit it far over her head.

But after a while, Don got tired
of batting the ball to his sister.
He wanted to play with boys.
He wanted to play on a real
team, in a real game.

TO THE
BASEBALL
FIELD

So he jumped
on his bike and
rode away.

He left Donna
at home,
all alone.

Later he came home,
happy and excited.
Donna asked:
"Did the boys let you
play with them?"

"They sure did," Don said.
"And they made me captain
of the team.
We're called the All-Stars.
And I'm going to play
with them every day."

So every day Don practiced
with the team.

Then one day a team
from the other side of town showed up.

"We're the Reds," they said.

"We want to play you.

Mr. Walter Smith, the plumber, has
put up this big silver cup—a prize for
the captain of the winning team.

"We'll come back and
play you tomorrow."

But on the morning of the big game
Don woke up with a terrible cold.
The doctor came and said,
"No baseball game for you today,
young man.

"You stay right here in bed."

Don was broken-hearted.
So was Donna.

"You get on my bike.
Take my stuff to the field,"
Don told Donna. "Maybe one
of the other boys can use it."

So Donna carried everything out
to Don's bike. She tried to load
it all into the little basket.
But the basket was too small.
Everything spilled out
on the ground.

Then Donna got an idea!
She put on Don's baseball suit
over her dress.
She pulled his baseball cap
down over her hair.
This way, she could carry everything.

Now she looked more like Don
than Don did himself!
But she didn't know it.

Out at the field the game
had already started.
"Where is Don?" everyone was asking.
"Why isn't he here?"

When Donna got to the field,
everyone thought she was Don.
They cheered and clapped their hands.
There was no time for her to explain.

"Don, you're late!"
the umpire yelled.
"Get over there
with your team!
GO TO BAT!"

Donna ran to the plate.

She was very frightened.

She shut her eyes tight.

She swung the bat at the ball.

And she missed!

She missed three times.

Donna struck out.

But that didn't matter too much.
Her team was a little ahead,
by a score of 2 to 0.

The game went on.
Then a terrible thing happened.

The Reds got two men
on base!

Then another Red hit a
high ball.

It went far, far up in the sky.

Donna ran to catch it . . .

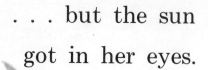

. . . but the sun
got in her eyes.

She couldn't see the ball.

Instead of catching it,
she dropped it!

Because of Donna's mistake,
the Reds scored three runs.

SCORE BOARD

INNING	1	2	3	4	5
REDS	O	O	O	O	3
ALL-STARS	O	O	2	O	

Because of Donna's mistake,
the Reds were now one run ahead.

A few minutes later,

the game was almost over.

Now it was the last inning.

The last chance for the All-Stars!

The first All-Star batter struck out.

The crowd booed.

The second All-Star batter struck out.

The crowd booed louder.

Then the third All-Star batter made a hit.
He ran to first base.

Now the All-Stars could still
win the game
. . . if the next batter made a hit.

But the next batter was Donna!
Now she was really frightened!
She knew she could never hit the ball.
She knew the All-Stars would lose . . .
all because she hadn't told them
that she was a girl.

But she went up to the plate.

The pitcher threw the ball.
It came straight at Donna's head!
She ducked. She closed her
eyes and swung that bat.

Somehow, that bat hit that ball.
Or perhaps that ball hit that bat!
Away the ball flew!

"Run, Don, run!" the crowd yelled.
"Don?" thought Donna.

"Oh, they mean me!" So she ran.
She ran faster than she had
ever run before.

She ran to first base.
The other All-Star
ran for second.

"Run!" the crowd yelled.

On around the bases
Donna ran!

The other All-Star came in
across home plate.
The score was tied now . . .
three to three.

But could Donna make it? . . .
The Reds' left fielder had
picked up the ball.
He was throwing it home.

Donna had to get there
before that ball did.

"SLIDE!" everybody yelled.

So she did slide—just the way
her brother had showed her.

"SAFE!" called the umpire.

"Hooray!" yelled the crowd.
Donna had scored the winning run!
Donna had won the game
for the All-Stars.

Everyone crowded around Donna.
The All-Stars laughed and shouted.

But Donna was not laughing.
She was afraid they would take
her cap off and find out
she was a girl.

She got down on her hands and knees
and crept out of the crowd.

She jumped on Don's bike.

She started for home.

But they saw her go.

"There goes Don!" the crowd yelled.

They all started after Donna.

When she got home,
Donna hid in the cellar.

The crowd rushed into the house.
"We want Don!" they shouted.

"I'm up here!" he called.

They found Don in bed.
They thought he was just tired
from the game.

Then Mr. Walter Smith, the plumber,
gave Don the beautiful big silver cup.
Don could have let everyone think
he had won the game.
But he told the truth.
"I've been here all day," he said.
"It must have been Donna
who won the game.
Where is she?"

Everyone started looking for Donna.

They looked under beds.

They looked behind doors.

They looked in back of curtains.

Finally they found Donna . . .

. . . hiding in the cellar closet.

They dragged her out,
and Mr. Walter Smith, the plumber,
gave Donna the beautiful big silver cup.

But that was not all. . . .

The All-Stars made Donna the
manager of the team.

Now she doesn't have to bat any more.
But she goes to all the games.
She is in charge of everything!

She takes care of all
the baseball bats. . . .

She is in charge of all the
baseballs . . .

. . . and all the baseball gloves . . .

. . . and the catcher's mask . . .

and the water bucket, too.

Donna keeps score at all
the games.

And the All-Stars keep on winning
more and more big, beautiful cups.

This year they won
23 to be exact . . .
the same number of cups
as Don and Donna have freckles.

DON

THIRD BASEMAN

THIRD BASE

BATTER

PITCHER

PITCHER'S MOUND

UMPIRE

CATCHER

HOME PLATE

THE BASEBALL FIELD

The Novels of

JOHN STEINBECK

A FIRST CRITICAL STUDY

By

Harry Thornton Moore

THE FOLCROFT PRESS, INC.
FOLCROFT, PA.

First Published 1939

Reprinted 1969

The Novels of

JOHN STEINBECK

A FIRST CRITICAL STUDY

By

Harry Thornton Moore

NORMANDIE HOUSE · CHICAGO

MCMXXXIX

CONTENTS

FOREWORD

THIS STUDY was from the first intended as an explanation
and a commentary rather than abstract criticism. A somewhat different and shorter version of it is to appear in
England, where it will attempt to present John Steinbeck
to a reading public that as yet knows little about him.

It is undoubtedly too early in Steinbeck's career for
assured generalizations about his work. Yet it must not
be forgotten that he is the author of seven novels, a play
and a volume of short stories, and that he is one of the
most widely read American writers of today. There is
enough material available to present a rather fully de-
tailed picture of his career up to now, and to provide a
basis for the understanding of his future work. This study
has no pretensions beyond that. It will deal largely in
particulars.

The biographical sketch, the check-list of first editions
and the map of the "Steinbeck country" should help
make the book a depositary of Steinbeck information.
The critical and biographical sections occasionally over-
lap: this was done knowingly, so each could stand up as a
separate entity.

The problem presented by the biographical sketch was
the biggest in the book. I have been working with the
material for more than four years, and have drawn information from many sources. Reluctant as he is to discuss

the biographical side of his life, John Steinbeck has from time to time generously provided me with necessary "physical facts," as he calls them, which have helped put the puzzle together. But he is not responsible for the bulk of the biography, which he will probably dislike intensely.

I have borrowed a little from the biographical sketches by Burton Rascoe, Joseph Henry Jackson, Lewis Gannett and Martin Bidwell, all of which appeared in magazine or pamphlet form after most of my biographical data had been assembled. I owe one or two important facts to Mr. Rascoe and Mr. Jackson, minutiae to the others.

Acknowledgments are due to the Viking Press, American publishers of Steinbeck's work, to quote from it; to Random House, Inc., whose Modern Library edition contains the only printing of Steinbeck's own foreword to *Tortilla Flat*, and to Charles Scribner's Sons for permission to quote at length from Ernest Hemingway's *Death in the Afternoon* and Thomas Wolfe's *Of Time and the River*.

I should like to thank several persons for their encouragement and help: Mr. Herbert Read, who first suggested this study; Mr. A. S. Frere-Reeves, who further encouraged its beginnings; Dr. Lawrence Clark Powell, pioneer bibliographer of Steinbeck, for permission to use what he has published (biographically and bibliographically) about Steinbeck; Mr. C. A. Sheffield, for invaluable information about the California backgrounds of Steinbeck's work, and — not least — Mr. George M. Dashe, whose interest and energy have made the publication of this edition possible.

H. T. M.

Glencoe, Illinois
March 29, 1939

A FIRST STUDY: THE NOVELS OF

JOHN STEINBECK

THE world of John Steinbeck's novels is a beautiful warm valley with disaster hanging over it. This is the essential feature of story after story. Steinbeck may change his outlook, as he has from the lyric to the sociological, or he may change his technical approach, as he has from romantic to dramatic narrative, but the valley-microcosm remains as the setting of his work, and his people continue to be foredoomed with an almost calvinistic regularity.

The lyric and romantic were the most noticeable ingredients in Steinbeck's first novel, *Cup of Gold*. This book appeared quietly in 1929, just two months before the stock-market crash that helped change the present direction of American literature. Steinbeck has not written another romance.

Cup of Gold is a fictionized life of the pirate Henry Morgan. Most of the action is laid in the West Indies and Panama, though a long introductory section tells of Morgan's departure from the Welsh valley where he had spent his childhood. The book is patently the work of a young man, an eager and romantic young man who was not afraid to let himself go. But if it suffers at times from overwriting, the book nevertheless gains a certain strength because of the lack of self-consciousness. Some-

11

times the prose is strained and artificial: " . . . so deeply ·
was she laved in a revery of the silver past" is a phrase
that may be taken as a sample of the weaker kind of
writing to be found in *Cup of Gold*. Yet the book contains many passages which may be set against these;
there are enough successful experiments of the picturesque kind Steinbeck was working on: "But again the
sun arose, like a white, fevered ulcer in the sky" is
forceful enough to take the reader into a living tropical
day, and there is effective suggestion of setting and
movement in such a sentence as: "While the dark was
down, the pirate scouts were ranging over the plain like
werewolves." The young author testing his strength
sometimes looked awkward when he slipped, but when
he didn't fail his efforts gave promise of remarkable
power.

Cup of Gold was adopted from an earlier story, "A
Lady in Infra-Red," which Steinbeck had written in college. The novel was completely re-written six times.
Steinbeck, who has always been susceptible to music
and often plays it as a preparation for writing, has explained that *Cup of Gold* was worked out—with the
various parts built up of parallel tempos—after the pattern of Dvorak's *Symphony from the New World*.

Another point of construction to be noted in this
first novel is the recurrence of symbols of concavity and
roundness. The image in the title is repeated at different symbolic levels throughout the story. If a list of
these usages were made, it could give some psycho-
analyst a stimulating afternoon. There are enough of
such images to be noticeable; some of them are apparently deliberate, others are doubtless used unconsciously.

The golden cup is first of all the moon mentioned by
the old Welsh bard which the boy Henry Morgan

wanted "to drink from as a golden cup." It is also one of the names given to Panama City, that smaller moon Henry Morgan drank from without quenching his thirst. And there is an actual cup of gold that Morgan finds among the loot at Panama. It has four gamboling lambs as a decoration on the outside—"inside, on the bottom a naked girl lifted her arms in sensual ecstasy." Morgan, who has come to Panama in quest of a beautiful woman he has heard about, hurls the cup away.

Some of the other uses of images of rondure and concavity include: the imagined hands cupped to shield a firefly in the bard's parable about the moon; "the wind, blowing out of a black, dreadful sky, was a cup of wine to him, and a challenge, and a passionate caress"; Morgan fondles the wheel "with a lover's fingers" as he guides the ship; Maracaibo is seen to have a "bottle harbor," and Morgan says of Ysobel "This woman is the harbor of all my questing"; Morgan, musing upon money, says "It could be cut in no more charming shape, either. A square would not answer, nor an ellipse"; the cheeks of the pirates are "shallow cups under their cheek bones"; and the dying Morgan has a vision of a grotto with his first love coming through it. This last is obviously a repetition of the motif of the cup Morgan found at Panama.

Not all these uses may be of equal importance, but a representative list was drawn up to show the frequency of recurrence and because the unconscious is so difficult to chart that anyone who wishes to make deductions about its manifestations must have as much evidence as possible. Such a list as this would be pedantic nonsense but for the fact that so much of Steinbeck's work is moulded around that image of concavity. It is never again used in this multiple way, with the central symbol reflected in so many small mirrors — it is minimized and subtilized in the later books. This symbol appears most consistently as a valley; it so figures in most of Steinbeck's short stories and in all his subsequent novels to date except *Tortilla Flat*. The valley symbol undoubtedly comes out of Steinbeck's early environment, the Salinas Valley in California. It is apparent in all his writings how the shape of the land has given shape to his thoughts: this valley symbol is most truly Steinbeck's Figure in the Carpet. We shall see, in considering *To A God Unknown*, how Steinbeck gives us some Freudian clues as to his feelings about valley contours. In his later books, which are more realistic than the earlier ones, the valley tends to have less obvious implications, though its symbolic value has not been destroyed. It is seen more objectively now, and has less of the pathetic fallacy in it as it plays a smaller active part in the stories: the valley has become the universe itself, and humanity assumes a more important role than it had in the earlier volumes.

The first time the valley setting appears in Steinbeck's work is in those passages about Morgan's leaving the place where he had grown up. This is the best sustained and most smoothly written part of the book. Steinbeck could reconstruct a boy's life in a valley because he knew essentially what such a life was like; and although he had not been to Wales, he had a feeling that he knew what it was like too. Because his mother's family came from Ireland, he felt a romantic kinship with Celtic lands and modes of thought. He researched extensively in the subjects of Welsh folk-lore and topography for *Cup of Gold*. One of the preparatory books he read with gusto was Borrow's *Wild Wales*. Steinbeck had visited Panama briefly, but the tropical setting is not so skillfully projected as the Welsh. An essay might be written on the value of a writer's visiting or not visiting the locale of an imaginative work about the past; the city known as Old Panama has nothing left but a broken tower, two or three fragments of buildings and a stone bridge—no other hints of the bright thronging life the place once knew: can a ruin seen out of the rhythm of its own time impart anything more than a dubious and sentimental value?

In every discussion of a Steinbeck story a good deal of space may safely be devoted to examining the author's power of evoking that quality we have no satisfactory word for—it is what the Germans call "Stimmung," and what we try to approximate with the word "atmosphere." Steinbeck is perhaps more interested than any writer since D. H. Lawrence in what Lawrence called the Spirit of Place. But this is only the lyric side of novel-writing. Lawrence, weary of humanity's blundering, came to loathe the traditional idea of "development of character in the novel," and the people appearing in his stories cannot be estimated according to traditional standards. Steinbeck on the contrary has worked within the established borders of novel-writing, so we may fairly use the customary methods of judgment when scrutinizing his characters and their problems.

Steinbeck was twenty-seven when *Cup of Gold* was published. He had not yet reached the stage where he could bring all his people fully to life. The woman in *Cup of Gold*, Ysobel (or, as she is known on the Spanish Main, "La Santa Roja"—the Red Saint) is a stock romantic figure. So is Morgan's friend, Coeur de Gris, who like Morgan is drawn to Panama by the fame of this woman's beauty. The speech of Coeur de Gris when he is dying shows how remote he is even from the plausibilities of a romantic novel: "My mother . . .

do not tell her. Make some gleaming lie. Build my poor life up to a golden minaret. Do not let it stop like a half-fashioned tower. But no—you need only build a foundation. She will continue the structure of heroic memory. She will make for me a tomb of white, inaccurate thoughts . . . " the situations coming out of such flushed language, and inspiring it, have something of its quality. For example, when Morgan finally seems to have Ysobel in his power, she draws a pin from her bodice, assumes the position of a fencer, and stabs him in the throat and checks. Morgan starts to kill her with his sword, but leaves abruptly, picking up a little monkey and stroking it as he goes out. There is more than one episode like this in the latter part of the book—they are situations pitched at melodrama but often falling into almost hysterical comedy. Yet Morgan is in some ways a living character, interestingly conceived and presented. Morgan of course has an advantage over the other people in the book because he is first set in motion in that magnificent Welsh valley. Further, Morgan is the only person in the story who in any way develops. Steinbeck showed that he could understand a nature like Morgan's, divided between dream and action. Morgan is a man of heroic energy who for a time holds all the Caribbean world in thralldom: but the dream is always ahead of the deed. The portrait is not done without humor, and Morgan is seen as an amusingly romantic liar. In later years he speaks of his first sweetheart, Elizabeth, as if she had been a great lady instead of a country girl, and he falsifies the story of La Santa Roja and magnifies the amount of her ransom. Morgan spends his last days in Jamaica, settled down amid honors, but he dies with his deepest longings unfulfilled. Not long before the end he makes an observation that

16

prefigures some of Steinbeck's later themes: "Civilization will split up a character, and he who refuses to split goes under."

It was good for Steinbeck to get *Cup of Gold* out of his system. He could probably have written a smoother book on his first attempt if he had been cut out to be a merely superficial writer. But the crudenesses of *Cup of Gold* were accompanied by signs of promise that gave some of these crudenesses a positive value: the streaks of poor writing could be seen as symptoms of troubled depths and a striving for poetry and for essential drama.

No one seems to have hailed Steinbeck as a coming master on the strength of his first appearance. *Cup of Gold* was either tepidly reviewed or ignored altogether by the critics, yet it managed to sell to the extent of some 1,500 copies. This was more than the combined sales of the original issues of Steinbeck's next two books.

The most positive reaction to *Cup of Gold* came in the form of imitation. Berton Braley's doggerel epic, *Morgan Sails the Caribbean*, published in 1934, borrowed some of the imaginary characters and episodes of Steinbeck's novel. Braley explains this by saying that "In the course of reading for background to the Morgan story Mr. Steinbeck's work was consulted as historical material, and the author of this ballad absorbed, as historical facts, incidents that were actually fictional inventions of Mr. Steinbeck." Steinbeck didn't object, and wrote "this troubador" (as Braley calls himself) a note which was printed in the foreword to *Morgan Sails the Caribbean*. This said in part: "It is far from unpleasant for a writer to find that some of his building or design has been found valid. Literatures are built in exactly this way. Please feel free to use what you wish of my work, subconsciously or consciously."

It was not until three years after the publication of *Cup of Gold* that Steinbeck's second book appeared. *The Pastures of Heaven* came out in the autumn of 1932 and received a fairly good reception from the reviewers, but the wide public was not interested. Today *The Pastures of Heaven* is the most popular of Steinbeck's three early books. It points the way to most of his subsequent writing, and readers who like certain features of the later work may trace the beginnings of them in *The Pastures of Heaven*. It contains the seeds of his sympathy with the Spanish-Indian natives, which later came into full flower in *Tortilla Flat*; it has in places some of that sentimentalized brutality which had appeared in parts of the previous book and was to be apotheosized in *Of Mice and Men*—and it has imaginative touches foretelling some of Steinbeck's greatest achievements: in his ability to suggest the spirit and the daily life of a community he gave evidences of the gift which was to help him create that living camp of strikers in *In Dubious Battle* and the grim squatters' camps in *The Grapes of Wrath*.

The Pastures of Heaven is not strictly a novel, though in categorizing Steinbeck's work we treat it as such: it is really a group of loosely connected stories that are given a suggestion of unity by an artificial frame. The title of the book comes from the valley where the action takes place, Las Pasturas del Cielo, so called by an eighteenth-century Spanish soldier who upon seeing "the Pastures" was as spellbound by their beauty as the latest twentieth century 'bus tourist is. This setting marks the first appearance of the "Steinbeck country," which is found between the borders of that California county where the scenes of most Steinbeck stories are laid—his native Monterey Country. The Steinbeck country, as it applies to his writ-

18

ing, may be said to be bounded on the north by Salinas and Monterey, on the south by Jolon and King City, on the east by the Gabilan Mountains, and on the west by the related line of mountains, the Santa Lucia range, which cuts off this region from the sea. A large part of this "country" is in the long Salinas Valley, and the Salinas River runs through most of it. There are smaller valleys formed by the abundant mountains, and it is one of these little valleys that furnishes the setting for The Pastures of Heaven. It is located about midway between Monterey and Salinas, on the road to Tassajara Hot Springs, and it is too small to be shown on most maps, though it can be found in the larger atlases. The real name of the place is an ironic antithesis to The Pastures of Heaven—it is actually called Corral de Tierra, Corral of Earth.

Irony is the keynote of this book, for the people who admire the valley from above see only its natural beauty and are kept in happy ignorance of the true condition of life in this seemingly idyllic place. Its history, from the time of that Spanish soldier who named it, is a long tale of woe. Most of the stories take place in our day, and the cast of characters seems to come almost directly out of Krafft-Ebing: here is a "normal" and "wholesome" community of farmers and tradesmen—and it is simmering with neuroses and insanity.

It is hardly necessary to explain that the characters are imaginary. Some of them are composites of people Steinbeck knew elsewhere, and they have no connection with the actual valley he happened to choose for his setting. The section of the book which has been most criticized for being improbable or overdone—the account of Mrs. Van Deventer and her mad daughter—is based more strictly upon fact than any other story in the volume.

19

Most of the characters in *The Pastures of Heaven* are but working sketches for an apprentice novelist: "Spark" Wicks, puritan and compensatory liar; Tularecito, the halfwit who identifies himself with the gnomes he has heard of in school, whom he goes digging for; lonely, parent-haunted Pat Humber, who secretly makes over the inside of his house to please a girl and then learns that she is to marry someone else—the destiny of these characters is typical of the destinies of the rest. The story of the Lopez sisters is Steinbeck's first display of interest in the *paisanos*, the Spanish-Indian peasant types for whom he feels an amused tenderness. Perhaps the greatest charm of these *paisanos* is their native ingenuity of rationalization. The Lopez sisters, who operate a little cafe, will never sell their favors for the coin of the realm and are insulted if they are offered "the money of shame" —but they will give themselves joyously to the man who appreciates their enchiladas enough to buy extra amounts of them. "The sheriff, he came? Now we are on the road. Now we will be rich. How many enchiladas, Rosa? Tell me how many for the sheriff?" But the sheriff had come for another reason, one that brought an end to the happiness of the Lopez sisters.

The two stories from *The Pastures of Heaven* that stay most distinctly in the mind after the book has been laid down for a while are those concerning Junius Maltby and John Whiteside. Perhaps Steinbeck is closer in sympathy to John Whiteside and his father and to Junius Maltby and his son than he is to the other characters: there is certainly more nobility, even if it is an ineffectual nobility, in their modes of thought and in their ways of meeting changes of fortune.

Junius Maltby is a little clerk with sick lungs who has to leave San Francisco's fogs. He is well educated, a member of a family that has lost its money. His health improves after he comes to the Pastures of Heaven, and he marries a woman who has land and two small sons. Junius falls into a state of happy laziness and does nothing but read. The farm goes to pieces, the two boys die in an influenza epidemic, and his wife dies bearing Junius a son — and still he reads. When Robbie eventually has to go to school there is nothing for the boy to wear but ragged overalls. He is mocked, but soon his imagination captivates the other boys, who disobey parental laws and slip out to the Maltby place where Junius and Robbie devise exciting games for them all to play. These good times come to an end when the school board decides to give Robbie new clothes. Mrs. Munroe, whose family is unknowingly the "jinx" of the valley, buys the clothes. When she presents them, Robbie drops them and runs. The wonderful days are over: the incident has made Junius think that the pleasant, easy life is hampering the boy. He decides to take Robbie back to San Francisco and, after twenty years, go back to work himself. In Steinbeck's range of values the simple, natural life Junius and Robbie had been leading was ideal, and going to the city would be the beginning of degradation. "Decent" people's meddling had driven them to this.

The Whiteside story begins in 1850, when Richard Whiteside comes into the valley and builds a new house —New England style, but of undecaying redwood. Richard Whiteside is from the East and is a Harvard graduate; he has a vigorous love of the land and the urge to found a dynasty. The health of the woman he marries permits her to have only one child, and it is while this son John is at Harvard in his turn that the father dies of pneumonia with most of his dreams unrealized. John's wife can also have but one son. John, a milder edition of

21

his father, has hopes for this son, William. Even though William is not interested in his grandfather's books, he seems bright and eager in other ways, and John hopes the boy will farm the land. But William falls in love with the trivial Mae Munroe, who wants to live in Monterey so as to be in the midst of the pleasures of a town. He marries her and leaves the fine old place that had been built for the sake of coming generations. As if the Munroe influence had not done enough harm, Mae's father comes over one day and suggests that John Whiteside burn the brush off his hills — and while they are out doing this, an autumn wind comes sweeping along and the great house catches on fire and burns to cinders. John says, "I think I know how a soul feels when it sees its body buried in the ground and lost."

These stories are all simply told; the perfervid style of the first book is missing. *The Pastures of Heaven* is written in clear and simple sentences; they lack the bold strength of Steinbeck's later prose and have not yet picked up his rhythms, but they represent a great advance over *Cup of Gold*. There are times when the writing falters and a sense of unreality breaks through speech and situation, but for the most part the book has a coolness and poise, for Steinbeck's natural gifts as a storyteller helped him through the difficult places.

The Pastures of Heaven is the work of a young man whose philosophy was not yet resolved: Steinbeck at this time seemed to believe in an unidentified and malignant fate. The harm that comes to the people who live in the Pastures is not the result of any human will, though in each case there is a human agent of catastrophe. The Munroe family, newcomers to the valley, put the burdens of their own past misfortunes on the lives of their neighbors. The Munroes are not aware that

22

they are instruments of destruction, and no one else in the book has this vision of them. Only the author knows, and he often has to warp his stories at the end to make them fit into this design, which is built upon the superstition of a "hoodoo." This helps to make the characters pathetic rather than tragic: the direction the book and its people ultimately take is towards sentimentalism.

STEINBECK's third novel, *To A God Unknown*, was published in the autumn of 1933. Its setting, "the valley of Nuestra Senora," is actually the Jolon Valley, lying below King City about thirty miles south of Corral de Tierro. The town described in the story is Jolon, which Steinbeck visited as a child, and the true name of the river that appears as the San Francisquito is the San Antonio. The scene is presented skillfully, for by this time Steinbeck's prose style was taking form. This is how the valley of Nuestra Senora looked when Joseph, the protagonist of the story, first saw it:

> The level floor was deep in wild oats and canary mustard flowers. The river San Francisquito flowed noisily in its bouldered bed through a cave made by its little narrow forest. The flanks of the coast range held the valley of Nuestra Senora close, on one side guarding it against the sea, and on the other against the blasting winds of the great Salinas Valley. At the far southern end a pass opened in the hills to let out the river, and near this pass lay the church and the little town of Our Lady. The huts of the Indians clustered about the mud walls of the church, and although the church was often vacant now and its saints were worn and part of its tile roof lay in a shattered heap on the ground, and although the bells

were broken, the Mexican Indians still lived near about and held their festivals, danced La Jota on the packed earth and slept in the sun.

Joseph has come out from Vermont in the fourth year of this century, leaving his father and three brothers in New England. The old man has made Joseph partake of a mysterious ancient ritual and has told him he will go out there too in a year or so: "I'll go right along with you, over your head, in the air." The father has died before the remaining sons come out to Nuestra Senora, but his spirit dominates Joseph throughout the book.

When the brothers and their families arrive from Vermont, Joseph becomes a kind of Abraham ruling the valley settlement, although Thomas is the eldest son. Thomas is plain and quiet-mannered, a lover of the animals and the farm-work. Another brother, Burton, is a rigid Puritan who is horrified at Joseph's admiration of fertility. Joseph tells Burton he feels like a bull: "I want increase. I want the land to swarm with life."

Joseph's love of fertility makes him dread and hate the drought, which he wishfully believes will not come again. His vaquero tells him about the drought of two decades ago: it lasted ten years, burning the land bare and killing the cattle. But when the rain came at last, in floods, the people in Nuestra Senora had a fiesta and shocked the priest by rolling naked in the mud. "They were happy. The wells were dry before, senor. The hills were white like ashes. It made the people happy when the rain came. They couldn't bear it to be so happy, and they did bad things."

The idea of drought is given a horrible emphasis by the nightmares of a sickly boy whom this vaquero, Juanito, protects. Juanito tells Joseph about them early in

24

the book: "He dreams he is in a bright place that is dry and dead, and people come out of holes and pull off his arms and legs, senor. Nearly every night he dreams it . . ." The symbiotic friendship between this haunted boy and the tender Juanito foreshadows the relationship of George and Lennie in *Of Mice and Men*, and these wasteland nightmares are the first signs of a motif that will develop importantly in the later parts of *To A God Unknown*.

Joseph in his worship of fertility goes to the extreme of insisting upon delivering his own child. Thomas's wife Rama tells him not to— "It's not the thing for a man to do" —but he replies, "It's the thing for me to do."

Joseph principally worships two symbolic objects, the huge old oak tree he identifies with his father's spirit and the great rock he finds in a glade. The tree is near his house; he hangs dead hawks on it and sometimes puts his hands on the wrinkled limbs and talks to it, addressing it as "Sir." He is confused when Thomas questions him about this, and he can only answer vaguely. But when he is scolded by Burton he defends his right to do what he pleases. Burton is disgusted and frightened by this "paganism" and leaves the valley, but not before he has secretly and cruelly girdled Joseph's tree so it will die. It is soon after this that the drought comes.

The clearing in the glade where Joseph finds the rock seems to have a spell of weirdness over it. The rock itself is "as big as a house, mysterious and huge. It seemed to be shaped, cunningly and wisely, and yet there was no shape in the memory to match it." The rock is "something like an altar that has melted and run down over itself." This becomes a place of destiny for Joseph. His wife Elizabeth is killed here one day when climbing the rock, and it is later the scene of Joseph's own death.

25

There are many other symbols in *To A God Unknown*, as in *Cup of Gold*, and like the symbols in that book they read, when wrenched from their context, like a list of psychoanalytic dream-images: there are snakes, bulls, stones, vultures, pools, brooks and many other natural phenomena playing significant parts in this story. Almost every turn people make in the valley brings them upon some new manifestation. Many of the symbols are sexual. In the light of later passages, even the first simple description of the valley takes on a new significance. It is a quiet preparation for the scene in which Joseph brings his bride home. The intention in the later passage is clear from the shape of the land and the way Joseph and Elizabeth react to it.

> The mountain was split. Two naked shoulders of smooth limestone dropped cleanly down, verging a little together, and at the bottom there was only room for the river bed. The road itself was blasted out of the cliffside, ten feet above the surface of the water. Midway in the pass where the constrained river flowed swift and deep and silently, a rough monolith rose out of the water, cutting and mangling the current like a boat prow driving speedily upstream, making an angry swirling whisper.

Elizabeth is afraid and Joseph asks her if it is because of "the narrow road and the stream below," and she says it is not. He tries to soothe her; at length she asks, "Joseph, what is it you want? What are you asking me to do?" After a struggle with himself to loosen his speech, he says hoarsely, "I want to go through the pass." He reassures her as he leads her through, telling her (with a phrase that echoes Lawrence's *The Rainbow*), "The bitterness of being a woman may be an ecstasy." She tries

26

to shut her mind in darkness, but she hears "the angry whisper of the monolith in the river." Then she feels a warmth in the air and opens her eyes, and Joseph says "Now we are through, Elizabeth. Now it is done." He aks her if it is bitter, after all, to be a woman, and she tells him, "It isn't any different. Nothing seems changed. I hadn't realized how beautiful the valley is."

All this is almost as great a strain on the reader in one way as it is on Elizabeth in another. And there is an equal amount of relief when it is over. This is a dangerous kind of writing: it has been done so often in comedy that the mind is conditioned to respond to it in a certain way. Not that this must necessarily spoil such effects for serious literature. But care must be taken to avoid what Ernest Hemingway calls "erectile writing." ("It is well known, or not known, whichever you prefer," Hemingway says in *Death in the Afternoon*, "that due to a certain congestion or other, trees for example look different to a man in that portentous state and a man who is not. All objects look different. They are slightly larger, more mysterious, and vaguely blurred. Try it yourself. Now there has or had arisen in America a school of writers who . . . had, it would seem, by conserving these congestions, sought to make all objects mystic through the slight distortion of vision that unrelieved turgidness presents. The school seems to be passing now, or to have passed, and it was an interesting mechanical experiment while it lasted, and full of pretty phallic images drawn in the manner of sentimental valentines, but it would have amounted to more if only the vision of those writers had been a little more interesting and developed when, say, not so congested.") In the literature of comedy this manner of writing is sometimes used in smirking concealment, to get a sexual symbol in humorous disguise past various censors—the censor of the consciousness as well as politicians who make a show of protecting public morality. And often in comic usage the intention is to create a funny effect by means of a ridiculous comparison, as in other types of humor. Steinbeck had of course a serious purpose, though he was using the technique of disguise as well as the technique of comparison. He was evidently trying to make his writing do somewhat the same thing Wagner's music does in parts of *Tristan und Isolde*. But unless this is handled with the greatest skill it breeds confusion in a prose that has to have some basis of concrete images. There are contours in nature and certain movements and elemental conjunctions which can be used poetically and symbolically to stand for phases of the sex act, and this can be done without comic results. But Steinbeck's scene at the valley-entrance is overdone: there are too many pictures, the symbols clash and change proportions, the shift of weather is altogether too servile to the desired effect. And the human actors going through various phases of symbolic tumescence and detumescence become absurd. Steinbeck attempted to do too much with his phallic geography.

Steinbeck could write a convincing love scene in the realistic vein, and proved it later in the book. This is when Rama comes to comfort Joseph after Elizabeth's death. The scene is almost completely described, and is written with smoothness and proficiency. This episode comes after Joseph's tortured mind has been indulging in the most inscrutable mysticism in the book: Joseph's arm is seen as a mountain range and his whole body as a kind of planet crowned by a world-brain. But the reality and ferocity of Rama's passion blows the mysticism out of Joseph for a while.

It is refreshing to get a clear scene like this; fortunately others may be found. There is a vivid presentation of the daily life in the valley ranches that comes through the subjective Joseph story now and then, and these passages are among the most successful in the book. The California which Steinbeck was writing of retained a frontier roughness that diked seepages of civilization from the outside. The valley Joseph Wayne comes to is not so primitive as the section of the earth on which Axel establishes his colony Sellanraa in *Growth of the Soil*, but parts of Steinbeck's novel are in some ways reminiscent of this phase of Hamsun. Although Steinbeck's writing has a distinct American flavor, it is at some levels more like the type of writing found in European novels of the soil than it is like the products of his fellow-countrymen. It must be carefully explained that the European tinge in Steinbeck's work exists in addition to its native elements of idiom, topography and psychology; it is a general coloring rather than anything else. It is really more apparent in *To A God Unknown* than in the other books, though it can be found at times in most of them. The presence of this attribute may not be due at all to any imitation of European writers, but may rather occur because his work, like his life, has an extensive natural background. Steinbeck spent so much of his boyhood romping through California's abundant forests that he must have some qualities of vision in common with the northern European writers who have been brought up under the shadow and influence of the great dark continental forests where most of the myths that underlie the story-telling and the dream imagery of the western world had their origin. Steinbeck lacks some of the traditional and hereditary basis of these writers, as he belongs to a newer culture, so the forest-lore can never

29

quite mean so much to his consciousness as it does to theirs. But he has some of this feeling, and it vitalizes his work. This does not always save it from its weaknesses: his people sometimes show a rigidity of conception and are motivated by expediencies of story in a way that sound European writers would never permit—and often these characters are mawkishly dealt with. But the stronger side of Steinbeck's talent is at least a protection against the specious cleverness that has infected so much contemporary British and American writing.

To A God Unknown had a peculiar and interesting origin. It was first taken over from a play written by a friend who suggested that Steinbeck try to novelize it. It was greatly altered in the process, and finally Steinbeck wrote all of it himself. It was at that time called *The Green Lady*, and the title itself was indicative of the change in Steinbeck's writing: it will be remembered that the woman in his first book was called the Red Saint, originally the Lady in Infra-Red, highly romantic in color and concept—we still have a "lady" in the early versions of this third novel, but she is a symbolic one, and the green is the green of the forest itself. Several publishers nearly accepted *The Green Lady*, but ultimately turned it down because of a forty-year hiatus in the middle of the story. In the latter part of the book the leading character, Andy, was almost insanely in love with a California forest. He was misunderstood by his prosaic wife, who read evil into his strange, almost aesthetic love for his daughter, whom he identified in some way with the forest-spirit. At the end of the book the forest was ablaze, and Andy walked sacrificially into it.

Steinbeck revised all this entirely in writing *To A God Unknown*. One of the episodes was recast and put into *The Pastures of Heaven* as the story of the Lopez sisters.

A few minor scenes and characters remained, but for the most part *To A God Unknown* was a completely new book.

Three supplementary characters who add great value to the book are Juanito, Father Angelo and Benjy Wayne. Juanito is the link between Joseph and the *paisanos* of the valley, who come so gaily to fiestas, who dance like pagans in the rain when the drought breaks. Juanito has a good deal in common with another character out of California literature whose brother he might almost be— Vasquez, that Waldo Frank on horseback who drifts through the pages of Jeffers. Father Angelo strikes a note of gentle humanity and tolerance that is needed amid such harsh surroundings. Leavening of another kind is provided by Joseph's youngest brother, Benjy, the jolly and undependable Wayne. Benjy appears in the story in a very minor role, but he is unforgettable. There is an exciting appeal about Benjy and his carefree existence, and even when he is only a drunken voice in the town at night he casts a spell. His death is typical of his life: Juanito, coming home unexpectedly, finds someone with his wife, and stabs Benjy in the back before he sees that it is Joseph's brother. Thomas tells Joseph about it and when Joseph asks whether they will have to have a coroner out and whether anything has been changed, Thomas says, "Well, we brought him home. And we pulled up his pants."

The long passages that have been quoted give a fair idea both of the good points and the ineptitudes in the prose of *To A God Unknown*. The writing often has the quiet strength that may be found in the description of the valley as Joseph first saw it. One important aspect of Steinbeck's descriptive writing that may be noted in that passage is its almost Cezannesque solidness: although

31

Steinbeck often uses subject-matter similar to that of the literary impressionists, his settings are never impressionistically presented. This is not to say that the writing in *To A God Unknown* did not sometimes veer out of control; the episode of Joseph and Elizabeth going through the pass shows that it did, and there are other examples of awkwardness and bathos. The mysticism is often confused or too deeply individualized to be understood: Steinbeck had still not found himself philosophically. Today he is no longer trying to write in this mystic vein, as he is working in what is generally called realism; but he doubtless still has a strong urge towards the mystic and will perhaps yield to it again sometime. With his expressional power more matured and a fuller experience behind him, his work of this kind could be impressive.

The most forceful passages in the story are those concerning the drought that finally appears. This blooms thematically out of the nightmares mentioned earlier: Steinbeck was still writing in the mood of music, and while working on *To A God Unknown* was continually playing Brahms and Handel. The drought comes as effectively as a symphonic movement that has had the way prepared for it, and those last scenes have a mounting horror as Joseph is left alone in the dust-dry land that becomes like a moonscape, with vultures flapping down to pick the bones of his cattle.

In Steinbeck's world, men who have loved the soil and worked in it have two great enemies. The first is drought, the second is the market and labor conditions imposed upon them by the social system. *To A God Unknown* depicts, as we have seen, the ravages of drought; in his succeeding books Steinbeck was to turn his attention to the social system. In *The Grapes of Wrath* he combines these two factors.

It is necessary to deal with *To A God Unknown* at some length in any full consideration of Steinbeck's work, not only because he had put into the book (often in symbolic disguise) most of his feelings about life after some thirty years' experience with it, but also because it is a valediction to his early writing period. After such an internal plowing up as this book represents, it was but natural that his interest should, for a while at least, turn outward. And his succeeding novels have marked different stages of that outward-going.

Steinbeck had manifested interest in a group in each of his first three books; there were Morgan's pirates in the first novel, and the next two volumes dealt with little valley communities. Yet in all these cases the interest was broken into bits and never quite blent into the whole. *To A God Unknown* has a more subjective point of view than the other two books, yet the community-pictures are more alive than the rest of the story, although they were meant to be subordinate. The fact that they stand out as they do is an indication of the direction Steinbeck's immediate interest was taking.

BETWEEN the publication dates of *To A God Unknown*, which demarcated the end of Steinbeck's first period as a writer, and those of that very different first book of his next phase, *Tortilla Flat*, there was a gap of more than a year and a half. During this interval (indeed, soon after the appearance of *To A God Unknown*) the first two parts of the short-story group later called *The Red Pony* were printed in the lone magazine which would accept Steinbeck's work at this time, *The North American Review*. Four years later, in 1937, the whole of *The Red Pony* was issued in book form in a limited edition; it was given to the wide public a year after that in the first collected volume of Steinbeck's short stories. The important point to remember is that *The Red Pony* is an early work, though it may seem otherwise because of its late appearance in book form and because its straightforward observation and its sense of control make its writing resemble the later books.

The Red Pony tells the story of "the boy Jody," obviously a partly autobiographical character, who is seen in relation to different phases of life at his father's ranch— the animals, the people, the surrounding country. The harshness of the world is always ready to make itself felt, but in the times between the descents of doom we again find the glow that seems to play over Steinbeck's work when he is writing of daily ranch-life. The story really comprises three stories: they concern the horrible death of a pony, the hard birth of a colt, and the return of an old *paisano* to the place where he had been born. This last-mentioned section is one of Steinbeck's finest stories, despite the too-obvious comparison of the weary old man with the spent old horse (a somewhat similar parallel was to be used with greater subtlety but no less trickery in *Of Mice and Men*). Yet the other parts of this story, "The Great Mountains," are effective. And there is something new: Steinbeck deals with the concept of private property in a way he had never dealt with it before. The old *paisano's* home had once been on the site of the present ranch, and when he was a boy he had lived there with his father, even as Jody is now dwelling there with his own father. The old man is first seen by Jody, to whom he says simply, "I am Gitano, and I have come back." Jody's mother and father try to get rid of Gitano, but he is as implacable as Melville's Bartleby. They think he is looking for work, but no, he is too old to work. "I will stay here until I die." But he is not permitted to stay, he is

34

worth no more to Jody's father than the useless old horse. It was apparent that a new yeast was working in Steinbeck in his first story of the dispossessed.

The Red Pony contains some of the finest prose passages Steinbeck had yet written. There is for example this account of Jody rising early in the California morning and going out to see his new pony in the barn:

> In the grey quiet mornings when the land and the brush and the houses and the trees were silver-grey and black like a photograph negative, he stole toward the barn, past the sleeping stone and the sleeping cypress tree. The turkeys, roosting in the tree out of coyotes' reach, clicked drowsily. The fields glowed with a grey frost-like light and in the dew the tracks of rabbits and of field mice stood out sharply. The good dogs came stiffly out of their little houses, hackles up and deep growls in their throats. Then they caught Jody's scent and their stiff tails rose up and waved a greeting . . .

The pictures here are superb, and the passage is improved by the break in the prevailing style made by the word "good," which may seem faintly out of key, though it is essentially so right, giving a touch of informality and warmth in just the proper place. It is the kind of risk a man who is writing good prose can afford to take.

WHEN Tortilla Flat, Steinbeck's first book to be widely read by the public, came out in the spring of 1935, it seemed to be a mutation in his career: the little company of readers of his previous books found it utterly different from what they had expected. While Steinbeck had dealt with paisanos before (the Lopez sisters, Juanito, Gitano) he had never given them such free rein and had never so fully exhibited his own comic talent. The book also seemed strange because its setting was on a hilltop (even those who had not distinctly been aware of the role the valley setting had played in Steinbeck's former work must have unconsciously felt the difference) and not in the bottom of a bowl of earth. But there are other features of *Tortilla Flat* that are the inevitable development of hints and barely traceable tendencies which have been mentioned in connection with the other books. *Tortilla Flat* has distinct sociological references; they are not overt, but they are there.

Tortilla Flat is a new kind of American comedy, concerned with "natives" of an unusual kidney, the paisanos who lead an exuberant rakehell existence in the uphill district above the coast town of Monterey. They never have any money but they can always manage to get jugs of wine. They are never really unhappy about their poverty, for they have a sense of values that projects beyond the material. Steinbeck loves them for this as much as for anything else. He knew the paisanos from the time he was a child, and during his depressing early years as a writer he used to visit their colony in Monterey when he was living in the next town. He would drink wine with them and exchange stories. A Monterey resident, Susan Gregory, sister of Jackson Gregory the writer of western stories, told him further tales about the paisanos; *Tortilla Flat* is dedicated to her. Steinbeck's central character Danny is a portrait of a squinting little bandy-legged paisano named Benny who is now dead, though his deeds are still famous around Monterey. Steinbeck filled in the picture with several other paisanos of various types, and constructed a kind of burlesque saga about their exploits. He was writing about a group of people whom the world in general would call insignificant, but he saw how their deeds, their quests, and the code they lived by could be used to parody the heroic tales of the past.

When Danny comes home from the war in the first part of *Tortilla Flat*, he finds that he has inherited two houses. The problem of private property is a difficult one for *paisanos* to solve under any circumstances: Danny mournfully reflects that he can no longer break windows now that he has windows of his own to be broken. While visiting one of the houses he sadly tells his friend Pilon, "I wish you owned it, and I could come to live with you." Pilon rents the other house, and agrees to pay fifteen dollars a month. He has never had that much money in his life except during the year he was in the army, but he can't worry about this because the rent isn't due for a month. Later he rents part of the house to his friend Pablo for fifteen dollars a month. Then if Danny ever asks for rent, Pilon can say "I will pay when Pablo pays." So life runs on in Tortilla Flat.

One of the most amusing sections of the book tells about Danny's love for "Sweets" Ramirez. By haggling with a pawnbroker, Danny is able to buy a vacuum-cleaner, cheap, for Sweets. In his eagerness he forgets that there is no electricity in Tortilla Flat. But this doesn't disturb Sweets, who shows the shining machine to her friends and walks around the house while her voice hums in imitation of a motor. Her friends try to belittle the present: "It is too bad you can't run this machine." — "I have always held that a broom and a dustpan, properly used, are more thorough."

But their envy could do nothing against the vacuum. Through its possession, Sweets climbed to the peak of the social scale of Tortilla Flat. People who did not know her name referred to her as "that one with the sweeping-machine." Often when her enemies passed the house, Sweets could be seen through the window, pushing the cleaner back and forth, while a loud humming came from her throat. Indeed, after she had swept her house every day, she pushed the cleaner about on the theory that of course it would clean better with electricity, but no one could have everything.

She excited envy in many houses. Her manner became dignified and gracious, and she held her chin high as befitted one who had a sweeping-machine. In her conversation she included it. "Ramon passed this morning while I was using the sweeping-machine." "Louise Meater cut her hand this morning, not three hours after I had been pushing the sweeping-machine."

But in her elevation she did not neglect Danny . . .

The story goes on gaily, through episode after episode. Some idea of its scope and of its status as a saga in travesty may be gathered from a few of the chapter headings: "VIII. How Danny's Friends sought mystic treasure on St. Andrew's Eve. How Pilon found it and later how a pair of serge pants changed ownership twice." "X. How the Friends solaced a Corporal and in return received a lesson in paternal ethics." "XI. How, under the most adverse circumstances, love came to Big Joe Portagee." "XII. How Danny's Friends assisted the Pirate to keep a vow, and how as a reward for merit the Pirate's dogs saw an holy vision." "XIV. Of the good life at Danny's house, of a gift pig, of the pain of Tall Bob, and of the thwarted love of the Viejo Ravanno." "XV. How Danny brooded and became mad. How the devil in the shape of Torelli assaulted Danny's house"—and so on, through other adventures. What has been borrowed from legendary tradition will easily be recognized. But the story Steinbeck wrote lacks a sense of completeness. If the unifying framework is too apparent in *The Pastures of Heaven*, here it is too faint. The events are most anecdotic, there is little organic development from part to part, and the closing phase has too arbitrary a motivation. It failed on the stage some two and a half years after its appearance as a novel, although put into play form by Jack Kirkland, the successful dramatist of "Tobacco Road." Considering *Tortilla Flat* in the light of an inverse parallel to the King Arthur legends, it will be seen that even the loose-jointed rendering of those stories by Malory has a more logical unity of development: the subject-matter has of course far greater depth and more possibility of time-expanse in which to work out an underlying consistency. But even though *Tortilla Flat* does not at the last provide the sense of ..armony which a more smoothly proportioned story should, it makes pleasant piecemeal reading, and is a charming comedy. And it had the virtue of being unmoral without apology.

Steinbeck later regretted that he had written the book. In the introduction to the Modern Library edition, he said that he had done the stories because they were true and because he liked them. "But literary slummers have taken these people up with the vulgarity of duchesses who are amused and sorry for a peasantry." It had not occurred to him that the *paisanos* were "quaint" or "underdoggish," or he should never have written the stories. But once they were published, it was too late to call them back. "But I shall never again subject to the vulgar touch of the decent these good people of laughter and kindness, of honest lusts and direct eyes, of courtesy beyond politeness."

TORTILLA FLAT was more than the beginning of Steinbeck's second period as a writer. His attempts to work out a group-philosophy have been mentioned—this book represents the first successful use of it. Danny and Pilon and the other *paisanos* are developed individuals and yet they are intrinsic parts of a group that has a psychology of its own apart from the individuals. Steinbeck's next novel, *In Dubious Battle*, which appeared early in 1936, is the fullest realization of his theories along these lines. This book is significantly built on the symbols of community and communism. The interest in group-psychology comes to the fore in the discussions of the doctor, who is present among the strikers to study their mass psychology. For several years Steinbeck had been consciously working out a "phalanx theory," and this is partly expressed through the medium of the doctor (with whom Steinbeck now denies any possible autobiographical connection), and partly through the working out of the story's essential complications. While he had been writing *To A God Unknown* and other stories based upon his past experience and his former ways of thinking, he had also been making sociological notes on the basis of biological observations: hundreds of billions of coral insects work together to make a strange and beautiful plant-like formation, and these formations in turn create atolls; this is like the people in the Middle Ages making the Gothic spire, working under a powerful and mysterious influence, not using their bodies as building material but using something finer and yet not material, and so on— these were the kinds of notes Steinbeck was jotting down or writing out in letters. This may not have been deeply original thinking, but it was consolidating a point of view. Such theorizing, as well as the neutralization of the problems of the individual and of the concepts of a generalized fate, helped to produce the new Steinbeck. And the change was conditioned by the disturbances that were rocking the social system.

In Dubious Battle was meant to be "just a story": after its publication Steinbeck said this and said it was also an attempt to make some kind of pattern out of the behavior of half-articulate men. He admitted that one's sympathy is naturally disposed to be with the strikers if one can see enough of the events of a strike, but he was trying to write this story without looking through "the narrow glass of political or economic preconception."

Some readers from the political Left criticized the book because they thought the strike-leader was an unreal figure. But Steinbeck was not trying to write a story of a party-line of a particular moment. The situation is reminiscent of the controversy that raged around Turgenev's character Bazarov in the last century: the Russian radicals were furious, feeling they had been caricatured in *Fathers and Sons*, but a few years later a younger and more advanced group of radicals rejected the opinion of their elders and called themselves Nihilists after Bazarov, whom they idealized as a hero to be followed in principle and practice. Those who criticized Steinbeck's portrait of his agitator didn't know that he had made the acquaintance of a communist district organizer who gave Steinbeck his life story. Steinbeck originally began a realistic biographical sketch of him in the first person, but later transmuted this into background material for *In Dubious Battle*. He was after all trying to write literature rather than a factual report ("Speak as they please, what does the mountain care?"), and in spite of this argument as to the book's ultimate reality, even its possibility, *In Dubious Battle* won the approval of most of the readers on the Left. Steinbeck had not been part of the proletarian literary movement that had been launched a few years before, but now he was hailed by the *Sunday Worker* for writing "one of the most impressive proletarian novels" its reviewer had ever read, while the *New Masses* said "Mr. Steinbeck talks United States. His sentences are packed with intense physical experience, whether it be the gobbling of a hamburger by a self-starved man or the impression made on a tired worker's mind by trees at twilight." Liberals also praised the book, and it even won a certain amount of respect from conservatives who agreed to consider *In Dubious Battle* as "just a story." Some reviewers said it was the finest strike or labor novel yet written in America. But the wide public didn't receive it with the same enthusiasm as *Tortilla Flat*, which had sold so encouragingly. The big fireworks were to wait for *Of Mice and Men*.

The foreground heroes of *In Dubious Battle* are two young agitators. One of them is already a veteran, a district official in what is never more definitely referred to than "the Party." He is the character some readers consider unreal, and it is true that he does many things no single human being would be likely to do or capable of doing. His partner is a greenhorn, Jim, who is helping Mac to foment and control a strike among the migratory fruit-pickers in a California valley. Jim and Mac have a double struggle: besides the difficulty of keeping the strike going against crushing odds, they have fierce internal conflicts between their momentary feelings and their devotion to the long view. Then, running through them and beyond them, there is the story of the background heroes—the group, in this case the "fruit tramps" they have goaded into action. These men have been almost dehumanized before the start of the story. Although California has an abundance of natural riches, labor conditions are about as bad there as they are anywhere in the world: the wealthy fruit growers who own a good part of the middle of California have created what is practically a feudal state. As Mac says in the novel, "This valley's organized like Italy."

The strikers' cause in the story is a justifiable one: the owners have waited until the pickers put themselves to the trouble and expense of coming to the valley; then the announcement is made that prices promised to be paid for the work are to be lowered. The "fruit tramps" are caught; they are practically forced to take the loss and stay to do the picking. The owners gamble on this, and they almost never have to get substitutes. People as poor as migratory fruit pickers can generally do no more than make a feeble protest. Mac brings Jim from San Francisco to the Torgas Valley to help him awake these men and stir them into life. The humanity of the men is restored by the activity of the strike: another thousand of them have been roused to resistance, and even though they engage in a dubious battle, even though their strike may be lost, its reverberations will be felt along other fronts. These workers learn an important lesson from the strike. They see the methods the owners are willing to use: they cheat the fruit pickers in the matter of wages, they offer inducements to some of the men to spy on their fellow-workers, they hire bullies to beat up the strikers, and they will even stoop to murder by ambush.

It was the most exciting material Steinbeck had yet used, and the reader finds that his own empathic urge has been enticed to the limit. Steinbeck has a greater blaze of power here than at any time before, as he brings life back to these men who had become so will-less and so lacking in vital qualities that they have been like those zombies of Haitian tradition who, supposedly existing in the twilight

43

world between the living and the dead, are said to be used by the plantation owners as the cheapest possible labor. When Jim and Mac have roused these men and organized them, they build a camp on the land of one of the smaller fruit growers, who sympathizes with their cause. Mac gets his philosophic friend the doctor to come from San Francisco and supervise hygienic preparations so the men can't be ordered off the land on a technicality; they dig irrigation ditches, the housewives of the vicinity give them material to make tents with, they get old stoves, and beeves are donated. The strikers and their families move in, and an intense daily life is created, a sense of community: for sheer writing, these sections of the book were the best thing Steinbeck had yet done.

It is interesting to notice that the incident which originally puts Mac in the good graces of the workers has him turning midwife in an emergency and safely delivering the grandchild of the man who was acknowledged as the head of one of the loosely organized bands of migratory workers. Mac has to pretend that he has had medical training: by using common sense and some practical knowledge, he is successful. It will be remembered that one of Steinbeck's previous heroes, Joseph Wayne in *To A God Unknown*, had delivered his own child. In *The Red Pony*, the boy Jody insisted on standing by while a farmhand cut the living colt out of the mare's belly. Both of these incidents seem apposite to the stories they appear in, but Mac's delivery of London's grandchild is just literary chicanery, and provides some justification for the charges that Mac is an incredible person. Steinbeck needed to get Jim and Mac on intimate terms with the leaders of the clannish fruit pickers, so he contrives to have them meet London at an opportune moment which Mac can make the most of. There is perhaps an additional

44

meaning to this incident, and if this is true the episode is sounder at the symbolic level than it is at the level of "plot" consideration: birth is used in several ways as a fertility symbol in Steinbeck, and here it may indicate a promise of something new and living come among these men.

The prose style of *In Dubious Battle* is a prose style grown assured and strong. It gives the story a resonance. It is responsible in no little measure for the living world Steinbeck creates on his page, as this sample passage about a dawn in the camp will show:

> Now the line of orchard grew sharp against the eastern sky and the parked cars were greyly visible. The buckets of coffee began to boil, and a rank, nourishing smell came from the bean kettles. The cooks ladled out beans into anything the people brought—pans, jars, cans and tin plates. Many sat on the ground, and with their pocket-knives carved little paddles with which to eat their beans. The coffee was black and bitter, but men and women who had been silent and uncomfortable were warmed by it, so that they began to talk, to laugh, to call greetings to one another. The daylight came over the trees and the ground turned greyish-blue. Three great bands of geese flew over, high in the light.

It will be seen that Steinbeck's writing has improved if this passage is compared with those quoted from *To A God Unknown*; the writing here is both more firm and more supple, the rhythms are easier, and the people fuse with the setting in a way they didn't in the earlier work. Steinbeck writes a hard and simple prose but it is not

45

without color, though the colors are hard and simple too. It is surprising to find him using a shade like ultramarine, as he does in the story "The Quail," which was an early, arty and experimental work. He must have deliberately limited the range of his palette in his later writing, but this doesn't mean that he fails to use effectively the colors at his disposal. Musical methods have continued to interest him, not only from the aspect of general structure but also as sound values; a friend of Steinbeck's has stated that In Dubious Battle "was carefully built acoustically, so to speak, and he pointed out to me that every scene had the sounds of another scene intruding into it to give it depth and a tri-dimensional quality." This is certainly not obvious, except in the case of repeated phrases such as "This valley's organized like Italy," and "He didn't want nothing for himself"—it is far less obtrusive than many other technical devices Steinbeck has worked out from time to time.

In regard to the "phalanx theory," he has said that he expressed it as completely as possible in the theme of In Dubious Battle and that it would be useless to repeat it in later volumes. But there is no doubt that it has had some influence on his subsequent work, and may for a while continue to do so. It is Doctor Burton, educated beyond the limits of the other characters in the book, who acts as Steinbeck's spokesman when the theory is being given dialectical airings in the foreground of the narrative. Doctor Burton tries to take a scientific view of the strike: "I want to see, Mac. I want to watch these group-men, for they seem to me to be a new individual, not at all like single men. A man in a group isn't himself at all; he's a cell in an organism that isn't like him any more than the cells in your body are like you. I want to watch the group, and see what it's like. People have said: 'Mobs are crazy,

46

you can't tell what they'll do.' Why don't people look at mobs not as men, but as mobs? A mob nearly always seems to act reasonably, for a mob." After a little more of this, Mac says the doctor is "too God damn far left to be a communist," and asks "What's all this kind of talk got to do with hungry men, with lay-offs and unemployment?" The doctor explains, "It might have a great deal to do with them. It isn't a very long time since tetanus and lockjaw were not connected. There are still primitives in the world who don't know children are the result of intercourse. Yes, it might be worth while to know more about group-man, to know his nature, his ends, his desires. They're not the same as ours. The pleasure we get in scratching an itch causes death to a great number of cells. Maybe group-man gets pleasure when individual men are wiped out in a war. I simply want to see as much as I can, Mac, with the means I have."

Steinbeck went outside his bailiwick for the setting of *In Dubious Battle*. But it was nevertheless laid in a valley, the small imaginary Torgas Valley surrounding the town of Torgas. The main incidents of the strike were drawn from events that had actually taken place a few years before in and near the city of Fresno, in the great San Joaquin Valley that lies to the east of Steinbeck's own, over the Gabilan Mountains, though the physical aspect of the setting is really the Pajaro Valley, north of Salinas (the region where the earth has recently been sliding).

STEINBECK returned to his home valley for his next book, *Of Mice and Men*, the short novel that was to make him one of the most popular American authors of his time. The ranch where the story takes place is supposed to be about four and a half miles below Soledad, on the Salinas River.

47

Of Mice and Men was written as an experiment. Steinbeck told his publisher not to disturb himself about the book if he didn't like it, and to send it back if it didn't interest him. But Pascal Covici was immediately enthusiastic about it and published it early in 1937. It was taken as a Book-of-the-Month Club selection and it entered the best-seller lists. Then as a play, adapted by Steinbeck with very little change, it ran for a crowded season on Broadway. The Drama Circle of the New York critics awarded it a prize for being the best play of the year.

Of Mice and Men tells the story of two drifting ranch hands, George and Lennie, who dream, as rootless men do, of a piece of land of their own, where they will "belong." They have never been able to work up a stake because big, blundering, simple-witted Lennie keeps getting them into trouble. He can never remember things. He tenderly loves puppies and mice, but always forgets about not squeezing them too hard, and kills them. Fabulously strong but very timid, he is docile under the control of George, the pilot-fish of the pair. George, little and clever, feels that Lennie has been given into his keeping. He holds him in check by telling him about the rabbit-farm they will have one day, where Lennie may look after the rabbits when he is good—George too is webbed in the dream. They come to work in the Salinas Valley, and it is there, amid the people they meet at the ranch, that their story is worked out, with doom hanging in the warm dry air.

Structurally, the novel was from the first a play: it is divided into six parts, each part a scene—the reader may observe that the action never moves away from a central point in each of these units. Steinbeck's manner of writing was coming over quite firmly to the dramatic. The process had begun in the latter part of *In Dubious Battle* (which the novelist John O'Hara once tried unsuccessfully to dramatize), where some of the most exciting happenings in the story take place offstage. After *Of Mice and Men* was published and the suggestion was made that it be prepared for the stage, Steinbeck said it could be produced directly from the book, as the earliest moving pictures had been produced. It was staged in almost exactly this way in the spring of 1937 by a labor-theater group in San Francisco, and although the venture was not a failure it plainly demonstrated to Steinbeck that the story needed to be adapted to dramatic form. The San Francisco *Chronicle's* report of the performance admitted that the staged novel had power, though it "seems slightly ill at ease in the theater . . . Its climaxes need sharpening," for "some of the scenes end lamely, tapering off without the pointed tag-lines that might crystallize or intensify the action. And there are certain passages of dialogue that caused embarrassed titters in the audience; it would do the play no harm to leave these out altogether." But when Steinbeck transferred the story into final dramatic form for the New York stage he took 85% of his lines bodily from the novel. A few incidents needed juggling, one or two minor new ones were introduced, and some (such as Lennie's imaginary speech with his Aunt Clara at the end of the novel) were omitted. A Hollywood studio bought the film rights to *Of Mice and Men*, but the picture has not been made yet.

Although there are few descriptive passages in the novel *Of Mice and Men*, Steinbeck's presentation of ranch life has once again the gleam of the living. The people, human beings reduced to bareness of speech and thought and action, are on the sidetracks of the main line of western culture. They exist in a hard reality, but most of them are susceptible to dreams. Some of them are lost

49

in a compensatory dream-image of themselves, others are
set afire by the wish-dream of George and Lennie. But in
one way or another all the dreams and some of the people
(the good along with the bad) are smashed. The spirit
of doom prevails as strongly as in the pages of Hardy or
of Steinbeck's fellow-Californian, Robinson Jeffers.

A writer deep in the lore of his own people feels (in
many cases unconsciously) a folkways compulsive: the
actual and mythical experience of his people helps to
generate his material. But the final shaping of it depends
upon the artist's own vision. Lennie in *Of Mice and Men*
is cast up from the midst of us and we all know him.
Baffled, unknowingly powerful, utterly will-less, he cannot move without a leader. And we also know many
Georges, good-heartedly trying to help the Lennies of life
muddle through; but all the while, despite their courage
and good intentions, none too certain of themselves.
John Steinbeck sees them as unable to prevent their
charges (and often themselves) from steering into catastrophe. In book after book his protagonists, tragic or
comic, are shattered, and it goes hardest with those who
had the brightest dreams. It is disturbing to find so many
of these likeable heroes going down so consistently in
spiritual defeat or meeting with a brutal death.

Violence without tragedy: that is the weakness of this
book. Socially considered, most of the people are what
could legitimately be called "tragic," but there is no
tragedy as we understand the word in reference to literature. On the social side, we have George's ritual of dream-
ing aloud with Lennie, which begins with this incanta-
tion:

> Guys like us, that work on ranches, are the lone-
> liest guys in the world. They got no family. They
> don't belong no place. They come to a ranch an'

50

work up a stake and then they go into town and blow their stake, and the first thing you know they're poundin' their tail on some other ranch. They ain't got nothing to look ahead to . . .

and continues:

> With us it ain't lik that. We got a future. We got somebody to talk to that gives a damn about us. We don't have to sit in no bar room blowin' in our jack jus' because we got no place else to go . . . Someday — we're gonna get the jack together and we're gonna have a little house and a couple of acres an' a cow and some pigs . . .

This has roots of social tragedy, despite the sentimental manner of its statement. (Steinbeck once said he writes this way because he is a sentimental guy.) George and Lennie and Candy and Crooks and some of the others are caught in this situation, they are lonely and homeless and yearning. But the social tragedy never really gets beyond that static proposition: its potentials are never exercised. It affords a background but it doesn't motivate the catastrophe.

On the literary side there is no authentic tragedy, which comes out of character. There is no basis for it. Even if we slur over the criticism that Lennie is a poor choice for a central figure in the story because from the start the odds against him are too great — even if we get beyond this and admit George as the true protagonist, we still don't find tragedy. George is no more than pathetic. He attracts sympathy because he has to lose his friend Lennie, to whom he has been so loyal, and whom he has to kill at the last in order to save him from the others. But because

51

this isn't genuine tragedy it gives the reader a brutal shock when George kills Lennie, and it cannot be anything else no matter how many little tricks have been used throughout the story to prepare us for Lennie's death. One of the most noticeable of these is the obvious comparison of Lennie with a worthless old dog that must be shot, as Lennie must be at the last.

It is true that Elizabethan tragedy ended with corpses and horror, and one doesn't protest against them when they are necessary ingredients to tragedy: it is the misuse of corpses and horror that is objectionable. It can become a trick. All that side of the *Of Mice and Men* story is crude and shoddy. The writing comes to reflect this, and although there are occasionally excellent terse descriptive passages, projections of atmosphere as well as superb descriptions of physical actions, the prose finally comes to seem as if it were stretched too tight — it gives an effect of bright artificiality. The projection is really too bare for narrative; since the main story is so slight it should have been filled in more at the sides. Its very narrowness emphasizes the awkward attempt to resolve pathos by brutality.

Fifteen of Steinbeck's short stories (three of them being parts of *The Red Pony*, previously mentioned) were published in September 1938 under the title of *The Long Valley*. These stories give something of a resume of Steinbeck's career, as several of them date back for a few years and others are more recent, two never having appeared in print before. The stories are mostly experimental; Steinbeck had been for a long time working out a theory of subconscious symbolism, by which certain elements of the rhythm and certain hidden symbols prepare the reader's unconsciousness for the ultimate effect of the story. Great literature does this automatically—when a too deliberate attempt is made to achieve such means, the result is often a failure, as we have seen in looking over *Of Mice and Men*. But it is interesting to see how Steinbeck works out the problem in these stories, which represent different moods and phases of the original valley setting. Some of the stories are germs of books —"The Raid," which tells of two men coming into a little California town by night to conduct a radical meeting, leads up to *In Dubious Battle*, "Johnny Bear" has a brutish idiot from whom Lennie in *Of Mice and Men* may have been drawn, "Breakfast" is a preview of *The Grapes of Wrath*. Most of the stories have the usual Steinbeck ingredients, ranch-life in the valley, contact with elemental things. There is plenty of good writing in the book; some of the stories are vividly sketched and work up to high pitches of interest, though a few of them are merely tricky. None of them comes up to *The Red Pony*, which (with an additional story about "the boy Jody" and his family) crowns the collection.

SINCE his first dip into local labor problems in *In Dubious Battle*, Steinbeck has become increasingly concerned with the social aspects of his California setting, which have provided the material for his latest novel, *The Grapes of Wrath* (April 1939). The articles Steinbeck wrote on the migratory laborers for the *San Francisco News* in 1936 lead directly to this new book; these articles were reprinted in a pamphlet two years later by the Simon J. Lubin Society of San Francisco, and a 1938 epilogue was added. This pamphlet, *Their Blood is Strong*, reveals how close — in sympathy and as an actual observer — Steinbeck is to his subject-matter. He has thoroughly explored the problems of the people he writes of, he understands these people, and his heart is with them. Besides the experience he had with them in California, he drove west from Oklahoma with some of them in 1937 and saw for himself the hardships that beset them on their western journey.

In *The Grapes of Wrath* Steinbeck takes one Oklahoma family and follows its fortunes on this westward trek and after arrival in California. Once again he goes outside his own valley, this time definitely into the great San Joaquin Valley, especially the torrid lower parts of it. The Joad family comes to Kern and Tulare Counties. Steinbeck is more specific about place references than he has ever been before, which is to be expected in the most realistic and Zolaesquely photographic novel he has yet written.

The Grapes of Wrath has a memorable beginning; the first chapter is at the top of Steinbeck's work. The dust storm comes in slowly, muffling the air and driving the people to their houses: "In the morning the dust hung like fog, and the sun was red as ripe new blood. All day the dust sifted down from the sky, and the next day it sifted down. An even blanket covered the earth. It settled on the corn, piled up on the tops of the fence posts, piled up on the wires; it settled on roofs, blanketed the weeds and trees . . ." The whole chapter has a symphonic effect, one of the most impressive in Steinbeck: it gets the story under way with a slow, steady rhythm, a rhythm that pervades the book and matches the slow movement of the dispirited people. The pace stays too slow throughout the novel, so there is no real quickening into a crescendo, but in these early parts the slow rhythm seems to promise a story of grandeur and epic movement.

Tom Joad, out on parole after serving four years for manslaughter, finds his home deserted when he gets there. He is told by a neighbor that the family has been

54

driven off the land, and is going west. This neighbor has refused to leave. He is a little crazy, and continually has to dodge the men who come looking for him. He catches wild rabbits for his food. He is as stubborn as old Gitano in one of the *Red Pony* stories, but not so quiet and resigned about being dispossessed:

> Well, the guy that come aroun' talked nice as pie. 'You got to get off. It ain't my fault.' 'Well,' I says, 'whose fault is it? I'll go an' I'll nut the fella.' 'It's the Shawnee Lan' an' Cattle Company. I jus' got orders.' 'Who's the Shawnee Lan' an' Cattle Company?' 'It ain't nobody. It's a company.' Got a fella crazy. There wasn't nobody you could lay for. Lot a the folks jus' got tired out lookin' for somepin to be mad at — but not me. I'm mad at all of it. I'm stayin'.

Tom learns that his family is at an uncle's, and about to leave for California. Before hearing this, Tom has turned loose a turtle he had caught for his youngest brother. The turtle had later tried to escape, turning southwest, the direction he was going when Tom originally caught him. And upon finally being given its freedom, the patient animal again makes its slow way towards the southwest — it is the way life is moving.

When Tom gets to his family he finds they have a truck, and are on the verge of leaving. California has allured people since it was the fabled land of El Dorado. Now these people who have lost their homes are making a great migration there. These Oklahomans were property owners once, but they have become dispossessed: the financial structure of the country collapsed in the depression, and the soil itself failed, for man and earth alike were inheritors of a social system that knew no safeguard

55

of planning. Mortgages were foreclosed during the depression, and property owners became tenant farmers, renting from the banks. After the dust storms, the banks decided to take over the land altogether; machine-farming could bring a slight margin of profit. The people were told to get out, and while they stood bewildered on the parched acres they saw tractors ridden through their doorways, crushing their houses. After the people were dispossessed, they were welcome nowhere; outside their own state they are called Okies, and it is a term of insult, a kind of successor to the phrase "poor white." California ranchers have drawn them westward with the bait of handbills promising work; thousands more men than are needed appear at the ranches where fruit or cotton picking is to be done, and the bosses can choose the men whose families are most desperate, men who will work for the cheapest wages. It is labor that used to be done by Mexicans and Filipinos who have left the fruit belt to white workers, "fruit tramps," who are so beaten that they will tolerate even lower standards of living than foreign labor. When the short-lasting jobs are over, the workers are pushed on. They are not allowed to camp anywhere for long — they might get the right to vote, they might organize, they might get relief status, and then they couldn't be bargained with. Deputy sheriffs are continually prodding them on, looking for excuses to burn their wretched camps, to take all those who protest against such treatment and jail them as "reds." The police themselves are tools of men and institutions higher in the social scale: Bruce Bliven has shown, in an article in *The New Republic* on the California organization known as the Associated Farmers, how the wealthy landowners of the state have the railroads and the gas and electric companies on their side, and how they all work together with the anti-union employers in the big cities. The whole emotional set-up of these vast landowners is antipodal to that of small farmers and dairymen in the Middle West and New England: Steinbeck, in his article for *The Nation*, "Dubious Battle in California," named Herbert Hoover, William Randolph Hearst and A. J. Chandler of the reactionary *Los Angeles Times* as typical absentee landowners of feudal California. Some of the worst labor conditions in the world prevail here: if a small farmer attempts to pay decent wages, the Associated Farmers come down on him like a wolf on the fold. It is a perilous place that has attracted the Joads.

Tom breaks parole to go with his family: Grampa and Granma, who have lived so long because they are "mean" (Grampa is Steinbeck's best character so far in the Dickensian vein); Ma, who controls them all; Rosasharn (Rose of Sharon), who is married and has the dignity of being pregnant; the cocky younger brother, Al; the children — it is a full and living gallery. Pa is what might be called a negative "Steinbeck man": Joseph Wayne, and Mac of *In Dubious Battle*, previous "Steinbeck men," have been successful midwives, as we have seen, but the elder Joad, who had been compelled by an emergency to deliver his own first-born, feels that he was inefficient and is being punished because Noah has never properly developed.

At the last minute there is trouble with Grampa Joad. He won't go, he won't leave the land he has known so long:

> I ain't sayin' for you to stay . . . You go right on along. Me — I'm stayin'. I give her a goin'-over all night mos'ly. This here's my country. I b'long here. An' I don't give a goddam if they's oranges an' grapes

57

crowdin' a fella outa bed even. I ain't a-goin'. This country ain't no good, but it's my country. No, you all go ahead. I'll jus' stay right here where I b'long.

They have to dope Grampa's coffee and then carry him onto the truck. They depart in the dawn, and their last moments before leaving are described in one of the supreme passages in all Steinbeck:

> . . . The light was sifting rapidly over the land. And the movement of the family stopped. They stood about, reluctant to make the first active move to go. They were afraid, now that the time had come — afraid in the same way Grampa was afraid. They saw the shed take shape against the light, and they saw the lanterns pale until they no longer cast their circles of yellow light. The stars went out, few by few, toward the west. And still the family stood about like dream walkers, their eyes focused panoramically, seeing no detail, but the whole dawn, the whole land, the whole texture of the country at once.

Grampa doesn't survive the uprooting: he remains dazed, and before they get out of Oklahoma he dies in a roadside camp, with nothing to be buried in but the borrowed quilt he died on. The family has no money for burial, so they dig a grave themselves, and put Grampa's body in it. They bury a bottle with him, containing some words Tom has scrawled on a flyleaf torn out of the Bible of another camper: "This here is William James Joad, dyed of a stroke, old old man. His fokes bured him becaws they got no money to pay for funerls. Nobody kilt him. Just a stroke an he dyed." Because they are paupers

58

with a man among them who will be hunted, they have to level off the grave and strew it with leaves. The whole scene — with the people in the glare of firelight, the men taking turns digging — has a homely and native essence. It belongs to the great midland prairie: yet the imaginative vision producing it gives it also something of a legendary quality.

An illiterate ex-preacher goes west with the Joad family, the Rev. Casy, who used to try to get the young girls full of the "Holy Sperit" but found himself invariably getting far different results. Casy is trying now to build a new philosophy, and is working out for himself the great questions of life: while he can't always explain his conclusions he is at least straining his brow over the problems. He is essentially an unreal character: he was apparently introduced to help give the book an underlying theme, and while Steinbeck puts even more vigor into him than in the Joad family, Casy nevertheless remains something of a contrivance, a sounding-board. He is at last cruelly murdered by a California vigilante who bashes his head in with a pick handle. Casy's last words before this, "You don' know what you're a-doin'," with the implied comparison with Christ, give his death the unreal quality of his presented life.

Things people say in *The Grapes of Wrath* sometimes have a flavor of staginess because Steinbeck was trying to reproduce speech exactly. This presents a problem: complete literalness in such matters doesn't necessarily simulate life in literature. American speech has been successfully fused into creative prose by perhaps only one writer, Ernest Hemingway. Hemingway doesn't attempt literalness, but adapts the rudiments of American speech-rhythm to his personal sense of cadence. He is monotonous and repetitious, but deliberately so, and with telling

59

effect. Although the speeches of his people have sufficient. relation to their source so they could be fitted to American lips, they are nevertheless not automatic reproduction — they have their own identity. These speeches are Hemingway's own distinctive instrument and at the same time a living suggestion of American utterance. The most successful speech-reproductions in *The Grapes of Wrath* are when Steinbeck approximates this condition in the chapters where he is trying to convey a general effect rather than literal individual conversations. These chapters occur at frequent intervals throughout the book; they are devoted to generalized accounts of the moving body of people, of the factors that drove them forth, of the topography of their journey, of what they will find at the end of it. These sections are in some respects the best in the book; they never quite function so efficiently as they should because the contrapuntal chapters about the Joad family don't always have the continuous strength to carry them. If the central narrative were more forcefully concentrated, these choral chapters would be set off magnificently, given more meaning and volume. But although they don't realize their full accessory value, still they have a power in the way they catch the essential spirit of that sprawling westering movement. And they pick out its vocal overtones; there is at times a resemblance to Carl Sandburg's *The People, Yes*. American names are named, places are mentioned, automobiles and native foods are identified. And all this is not literal speech reproduction, but a swelling musical suggestion of it that gives a far greater sense of "reality" than literal reporting. These chapters have an American resonance.

Steinbeck had great material for the central narrative part of his story: perhaps he was too much aware of this, took too much for granted. For although these sections of the book are handled smoothly, well written for the most part, and crowded with living people, the main story never quite comes to life in the way it should. This may be partly because the Joad group is too well-balanced; even if Ma Joad and Tom are brought into focus oftener than the others, neither of them really arouses our fullest empathy. And there isn't a continuity of suspense, a mounting excitement, as there was in *In Dubious Battle*. Here the material is more maturely dealt with, the people and incidents are more plausible, there is greater scope, yet the story has no moving crisis. The book was not written with the passion that went into *In Dubious Battle*, and it lacks that novel's compulsion of participation.

Steinbeck's imagination was often fundamentally right when he was working out the problems of this book; he called up some excellent metaphors. But they are presented too deliberately, without spontaniety and passion, and they don't illuminate the text so intensely as they might. As an example, we may examine the passage about the tractors, the "snub-nosed monsters" invading Oklahoma, driving people off the land, cracking the houses and fences to splinters. There is this description of the driver and his work:

> The man sitting in the iron seat did not look like a man; gloved, goggled, rubber dust mask over nose and mouth, he was part of the monster, a robot in the seat. The thunder of the cylinders sounded through the country, became one with the air and the earth, so that earth and air muttered in sympathetic vibration. The driver could not control it — straight across country it went, cutting through a dozen farms and straight back. A twitch at the controls could swerve the cat', but the driver's hands could not twitch

because the monster that built the tractor, the monster that sent the tractor out, had somehow got into the driver's hands, into his brain and muscle, had goggled him and muzzled him — goggled his mind, muzzled his speech, goggled his perception, muzzled his protest. He could not see the land as it was, he could not smell the land as it smelled; his feet did not stamp the clods or feel the warmth and power of the earth. He sat in an iron seat and stepped on iron pedals. He could not cheer or beat or curse or encourage the extension of his power, and because of this he could not cheer or whip or curse or encourage himself. He did not know or own or trust or beseech the land. If a seed dropped did not germinate, it was nothing. If the young thrusting plant withered in drought or drowned in a flood of rain, it was no more to the driver than to the tractor.

There is some good writing here, and originally the metaphor was cleverly conceived. But at last it comes to seem as if it were too coldly written down, the sentences are simply laid end to end, and the imaginative possibilities of the symbol don't come up living from the page. This should have been done in a few simple, warm strokes that would have made this goggled figure into a hideous and haunting demon. The effect would be double: there would be not only the horror of the despoliation of the land, there would also have been an unforgettably ghastly symbol of the doom that was hagriding the people of the story. It is impossible not to reflect what Thomas Wolfe would have made of this. Despite his annoying prolixity, Wolfe had a power of summing up experience in such symbols and stamping them forever on his readers' minds. And he once used an image similar to this one, in *Of Time and the River*, where he described a race between two trains. Wolfe in this case gives the reader a feeling of participation: he projects the excitement of the passengers, the Pullman porter, the men of the train crews. We get a sudden picture of one of the fireman, "balanced on the swaying floor, his face black and grinning, his eyes goggled like a demon, and lit by the savage glare of his terrific furnace . . ." This is written with passion, and despite the excess weight of the last adjective, the passage emerges into life. The interest is continued, the rivalry between the sets of passengers and train crews intensified. As the small train pulls away from the Limited for a while, the porter, chuckling "with a tone of reproof and disbelief," says to himself:

> Dey ain't got no right to do dat! Dey ain't got no right to run by us like we wasn't here! . . . Dey ain't nothin' but a little ole Philadelphia local! Dey're not supposed to make de time we is! We's de Limited! We got de outside rail! . . . But Lawd, Lawd! Dat didn't help us none today. Dey've gone right on by us! We'll never ketch dem now!

But later, when the smaller train is overtaken, we have another glimpse of that fireman, standing in the cab of the locomotive, "arms akimbo, black and grinning . . ." Wolfe could make a train-ride, with the passing and re-passing of two trains, read like some contest out of an epic. He could have made this tractor-driver, who has a greater potentiality than the grinning fireman had, into a compelling figure of American social mythology.

Sometimes in this book Steinbeck's writing-power fails, and he slips into the literary. The blood-ripe sun

63

that was so vivid in an early passage about the dust storms appears to poor advantage in a later scene: "A large red drop of sun lingered on the horizon and then dripped over and was gone, and the sky was brilliant over the spot where it had gone, and a torn cloud, like a bloody rag, hung over the spot of its going." This kind of writing, which is essentially "indoor" and literary in contrast to the authentic natural descriptions Steinbeck is capable of, can spoil important parts of the story. It does so in the episode where Ma Joad goes down to Tom's hiding-place to warn him that he is again in danger of being caught, this time for killing the vigilante who had murdered Casy. Ma, bringing him a plate of food, has to sneak out of the camp and go down to the place where Tom is hiding by the river. It is a moment of high suspense, but the suspense is impaired when we read: "Over the sky a plump black cloud moved, erasing the stars. The fat drops of rain scattered down, splashing loudly on the fallen leaves, and the cloud moved on and unveiled the stars again." This is strained, bookish writing, the stars being erased by a plump cloud, and so on, and there is a confused image with clouds being erased at one moment and unveiled the next. As yet the general health of Steinbeck's writing has not altogether overcome his inclination to the gaudy, and although these defects are being minimized, it is jarring to find them injuring passages that need sustained dramatic tension.

As some of the excerpts already given from *The Grapes of Wrath* may indicate, there are plenty of fine descriptive bits all the way through — cold dawns in roadside camps, the memorable night pilgrimage over the sultry desert, glimpses of bright California valleys with their orchards and cotton fields, and the rainstorm and flood at the end of the book. The incidental parts of *The Grapes of Wrath* are the best, as in other Steinbeck books. The people met on the road, the life of the camps, the struggles of the Joad family: these fragments are unforgettably presented. Steinbeck understands the lives of these people, their thoughts, their behaviour — and he understands their mythology, a queer mixture of half-digested Christianity and profaneness of utterance and elemental farmyard knowledges. (Their amorous anecdotes are about bulls and heifers, the figures of speech of these people are drawn from the barnyard animals and the growth of crops.) All new experience is a basis for further legendry for them: in the government camp the Joads live at for a while, they see and use toilets for the first time, and the two young children of the family think they have broken one of the toilets when they flush it. Also there is a woman in the camp who had also never seen toilets before, and began to use them as washtubs — the roaming Joads will scatter her story far and wide, and will help make it a part of American folk-history.

The Joads eventually have to leave the government camp, and with great regret; there are no jobs near it, they have to move on. There are two other kinds of camps: those constructed by the squatters themselves, and those belonging to the bosses. The squatters invariably call each of their crude camps Hooverville. The Joads get out of one of these just before it is burned by men wearing trench helmets and American Legion caps. The bosses' camps have their own stores where the migrants are compelled to buy and are cheated. Steinbeck wrote in *The Nation* that these camps have only one toilet for every two or three hundred persons, and that when a member of the Growers' Association suggested that separate toilets be provided for men and women, he was accused by his fellow-members of being "kind of com-

munistic." It is well-known that the California landowners are incessant red-baiters, but perhaps it is not so
widely known that the Nazi Bund's *Deutscher Weckruf
und Beobacher* (edited by Fritz Kuhn) has praised them
because "the informed Associated Farmers of California
are already promoting a nationwide organization of
American vigilantes — a *posse comitatus* — specific legal-
ization of vigilantism in a determined effort to save the
Republic."

They are saving the Republic from people like the
Joads, long-term Americans whose forbears "fit" in the
Revolution. *The Grapes of Wrath* may become the *Uncle
Tom's Cabin* of these migrant workers. It may do for them
what Dickens' *Nicholas Nickelby* did for the persecuted
boys in small English board schools, what Melville's
White Jacket did for the sailors who were being flogged
in the American fleet, what Upton Sinclair's *The Jungle*
did towards cleaning up the meat-packing industry. *The
Grapes of Wrath* will probably have a large sale, and in
some quarters will certainly be a *succes de scandal*. As far
as social implications go, it is perhaps the most per-
suasively revolutionary novel published in America, and
it is in the van of the proletarian movement in literature,
without officially being a part of that movement. In some
sections of California the book will probably be sold
under the counter, as *In Dubious Battle* was. *The Grapes
of Wrath* consistently uses language that will give puri-
tans the ecstacy of a good shock: but the Joads of life, so
close to the most elemental manifestations of sex and
death, know of no other way to speak. This novel has the
displays of brutality usually found in a Steinbeck book;
some of the natural deaths are gruesome enough (Ma
Joad lying all night beside Granma's body, knowing
Granma was dead but keeping it a secret so there would

be no delay as the truck went over the oppressively hot desert) — and there are harsh killings. The book has an Old Testament grimness.

It resembles the Bible in other ways too. The exodus of the dispossessed looking for their promised land has a familiar ring: they behold it from a mountain top, but upon their descent into the valley they do not find Canaan. The book ends with them still in the wilderness of frustration — how long it will take them to get out of this the story does not indicate. Tom may be the Joshua to come.

Not that Steinbeck was necessarily attempting a literal parallel, as Joyce does in *Ulysses*. But these ancient tales have patterns of human experience that are continually being repeated. There is a peculiar feature of this book which may partially reveal how much Steinbeck was unconsciously motivated by the Bible: although his sentences are taut, and have none of the flowing rhythm of Scripture as we know it, Steinbeck begins an astonishing number of these sentences with the word "and," in Biblical tradition. These beginning "and's" are so numerous, and in most cases so unnecessary, that they are notable; such a way of writing is entirely new in Steinbeck, and isn't quite in keeping with his tight prose-style. It may have been partly deliberate, as the Bible-story parallel may have been deliberate in a general way (certainly there is no intricate matching of episode with episode). But the general comparison is evident, whatever its stimulus may have been.

The Grapes of Wrath has certain elements in common with classics other than the Bible — with the great sagas and with all tales of exile and wanderings and adventure. (It will be remembered how *Tortilla Flat* parodied some of these classics.) Because of their American clothing, the incidents in *The Grapes of Wrath* may seem to be no more than things that happened on an American journey, but regarded in outline most of them seem part of a vast mythos. One thing is certain: the author knows something of the form of the *Odyssey*, the *Divine Comedy*, *Don Quixote*. Attempts of this kind have been made in America before, though not so many as it would seem the bigness of the place should induce. Thomas Wolfe's series of novels about Eugene Gant was meant to have such scope, but the completed parts that were published expose a tremendous fault: the books are centered too much in a single person, there is ultimately no blend of individual and universal. Wolfe's writing had a magnificent careless vigor and he could create vital characters outside his self-identified protagonist, but he seemed to lose perspective as his series progressed, and the reader is weary of Eugene Gant by the end of *Of Time and the River*. There was less and less of the outside world which Wolfe could so energetically picture, and more and more of Eugene's elephantiasis of soul-pain. The only American who has successfully created life-in-literature on the scale of the great writers of the earth is Herman Melville: individuals fuse with the world of the Pequod in that wild and mystic hunt after the white whale Moby-Dick. *The Grapes of Wrath* falls far short of such a book as that, not only because it lacks the intensity of a *Moby-Dick* but also because no compounding agent can bring the two elements of the story organically together: it is almost the opposite of Wolfe's case, for here the universal has more valid life and movement than the individual. This book might be judged by different standards if it were purely a group-novel. But it is not; it has phases of the traditional as well as of the collective, which has in any event not yet fully justified itself as an art-form. There is

68

a fundamental weakness in *The Grapes of Wrath*, and it is just this lack of force in the center of the story: it seems as if Steinbeck had done all in his power to give the novel verisimilitude and movement, had assembled all the required ingredients for a great book, and then failed to provide it with proportioned and intensified drama.

There is no vital conflict in *The Grapes of Wrath*. The story divides into two parts: first there is the departure from Oklahoma and the westward pilgrimage, then there is the California experience. This latter part remains static because it is a chronicle of the way the migratory workers are kicked around. No conflict is created because these trampled people don't fight back. It is a stirring picture of California's rotten social-economic-political conditions, and might be regarded as a deepening of the background material of *In Dubious Battle*. But that presented a conflict in dramatic terms; the double implication at the end of *The Grapes of Wrath* — that life will go on, and that Tom will work for the common good — is too quiet to resolve the issues that have been raised.

Several things in the story are never rounded off satisfactorily. The disappearance of Rosasharn's husband, Connie Rivers, leaves some unfinished business; it is too abrupt, and we feel we should not be through with Connie yet. The case of Noah Joad is somewhat similar, and his staying on at Needles, at the parched edge of California, has a false chime. Noah finds a river, and it lures him. His explanations are not convincing, and the writing is unreal: "Tom, I ain't a-gonna leave this here water. I'm a-gonna walk on down this here river . . . No. It ain't no use. I was in that there water. An' I ain't a-gonna leave her. I'm a-gonna go now, Tom — down the river. I'll catch fish an' stuff, but I can't leave her. I can't . . . You tell Ma, Tom." The story gets incredible here.

Noah is not made of the same stuff as Lennie in *Of Mice and Men*, but here he is talking as Lennie would have talked and doing what Lennie would have wanted to do. He walks away down the river through the willows, and Tom watches him; we never see Noah again.

Rivers and thickets of willows on the riversides have been playing an increasingly important part in recent Steinbeck books. In each of his last three novels there has been a hiding-place by a river; Jim and Mac have such a hideout in *In Dubious Battle*, the last scene of Lennie's fateful drama is acted out in just such a setting in *Of Mice and Men*, and in this book Tom eventually hides in a similar place. This must mean something in relation to the enclosing valley-symbol, which at the easiest level of interpretation must itself be invested with some kind of earth-mother meaning. The thicket by the river meant safety and comfort to Mac and Jim, to George and Lennie, and in this book two different river-thickets mean these things to two entirely different kind of men. Remembering Joseph Wayne, who in *To A God Unknown* observed "a curious femaleness about the interlacing boughs and twigs, about the long green cavern cut by the river through the trees and the brilliant underbrush," it is difficult not to conclude that this second most persistent symbol in Steinbeck is another phase of sexual geography.

The Grapes of Wrath is packed with meanings that may be partly understood in terms of his previous tendencies, though there are new beginnings which may lead to future developments. One of the most picturesque episodes in this book is the meeting of Tom and Al with the one-eyed man from whom they get a flashlight and a socket wrench one night in the middle of New Mexico. The first description of him is significant: "A specter of a man came through the dark shed." He is one-eyed and bitter, cursing his boss, who as a dealer in second-hand autos and spare parts is the successor to the sly horse-trader of yesterday. Tom and Al have a fairly long chat with this rather hideous one-eyed man who would like to go to California with them but is refused because the Joads are overloaded as it is. Tom cheers him up, and the man, still railing against his boss, gives Tom a bargain price on the socket wrench that will make the rest of the trip possible, and sells him his flashlight cheaply too. And despite the prevailing rapid nasal American talk, the whole scene afterwards floats in the mind like a piece of an epic.

This one-eyed protestant is only a single unit among the middle-men who hate to oppress the wanderers of the story, but are usually compelled to do so by those in power. The people themselves are warmly generous, and there is almost a collective family-sense among all the migrant workers. And every now and then someone from the other side steps out of the ranks of brutes and shows a human streak. One of the most striking conversations in the story is that between Ma Joad and the little man at the company store at the Hooper ranch: at first he enjoys her discomfort when she finds how high the prices are and how far away the nearest town is, but her intrinsic gentleness touches some chord in him that first shames him and then brings out his latent decency, so he lends her enough money to get sugar for her men's coffee.

It is Ma Joad's words that give the story the double implication of its ending. She has said "They ain't gonna wipe us out. Why, we're the people — we go on." And Rosasharn helps to prove this, for even if her own child has been born dead, Rosasharn can still give life. This final incident is not without the sense of contrivance

71

which Steinbeck can't seem to get away from: the floods have to come to the Joads' box-car camp and drive them forth to the shelter of a dry barn where Rosasharn can be brought into contact with the starving man. But even though the incident is so obviously "planted," it is skillfully lifed into a symbol. It is out of Maupassant, but while in his story the situation has a merely physical meaning, here the episode magnifies Ma Joad's statement of the life-principle: "We're the people — we go on."

The other phase of the ending is supplied by Ma Joad's last visit to Tom. He will have to be a fugitive the rest of his life — if he ever gets into trouble and has his fingerprints taken, he will be sent back to Oklahoma to be imprisoned again for breaking parole. He has killed two men. He could easily become an outlaw like Pretty Boy Floyd, whom his mother speaks of: "I know'd Purty Boy Floyd's ma. He wasn't a bad boy. Jus' got drove in a corner." Tom is in a corner too, but instead of taking the easy way out, bitterness and frustration and banditry and murder, he has decided to work towards some of the things Casy was finding out before the defenders of liberty murdered him: Tom has been given a sense of social justice and he wants to work with people, organize them against the crushing system. He will fight the dubious battle to help lead his people out of the wilderness.

Whether Steinbeck will continue Tom's story or whether he will consider that all this is behind him and begin a new phase of his own career, only the future can tell. But this much is certain: up to this time he has gone farther than any other American writer towards being the poet of our dispossessed.

A BIOGRAPHICAL SKETCH OF

JOHN STEINBECK

SALINAS is ten miles inland from the notch Monterey Bay makes in the California Coast. The town was settled about 1858, and since 1872 has been the seat of Monterey County, of which John Steinbeck's father was treasurer for many years. Salinas lies near the north end of the "long valley" whose checkerboard farms produce lettuce, cauliflower, beets, fruit and grain in one of America's richest agricultural regions. To the east of the valley the Gabilan Mountains rise, hill ranches on the slopes, black-green belts of pinewoods, and—just above Soledad—Vancouver's Pinnacles thrusting up their spire-like rock formations. On the west the Santa Lucia range cuts off the Salinas Valley from the coast: the flanks of these mountains carry the burden of sequoia forests, there are great passes of broken granite, and fogs from the sea are often tangled in the pine-crested heights.

The city of Salinas is a small industrial center touched by two railroads. There are machine shops of various kinds; one of the chief industries is the preparation of rubber for commercial uses. The town has several flour mills, and there is a large beet-sugar factory nearby. Salinas has frequently been the scene of strikes, particularly those involving the valley's lettuce-workers.

John Ernst Steinbeck, Sr., was born in the state of

Florida during the Civil War, and came to California at the age of sixteen. He married Olive Hamilton* of San Jose, who had been teaching school since she was sixteen. She had taught, among other places, at Big Sur, where the Santa Lucias break off to meet the coastline, and at the village of Peachtree, "near the mustang grade" in the Gabilan Mountains. Steinbeck, Sr., was of Prussian and New England stock; his wife's forebears had come from northern Ireland.

John Ernst Steinbeck, Jr., was born at Salinas on February 27, 1902. He was the only boy in the family. One of his sisters, Esther, became a home-demonstration agent at Redding, in the northern part of the state, and another sister is Mrs. Carrol Rodgers of Watsonville, near Salinas. Both of the Steinbeck parents died several years ago.

A friend has described Steinbeck's home-life as having been "definitely bourgeois." He must have been a somewhat solemn child, judging from the temperament of "the boy Jody" in The Red Pony, who seems to be a partly autobiographical character. Steinbeck has remarked that children are wise rather than gay.

There was much to make life interesting for a boy in that region: readers of The Red Pony will recall how impressed Jody was with the mountains that lifted above him—the Gabilans were "jolly," but the mountains on the coast side seemed to have a menace. It is evident from all his writing how the fertile bed of the valley attracted Steinbeck; it was full of living and growing things, cattle and the fruit and grain and vegetables being raised and produced there. El Camino Real, which

*The biographical sketch in Who's Who in America, presumably prepared by Steinbeck, gives her maiden name as Hammond, but a letter from Steinbeck says it was Hamilton.

had been the king of Spain's highway, twined across the valley from one crumbling mission to another. Steinbeck as a child often visited Monterey, the most romantic of California towns. The Spaniards had named and claimed it just three hundred years before he was born; in the 1700's the principal California mission, the San Carlos, was built there, and in the following century Monterey was capital of the Bear Flag republic. Monterey is still a picturesque and interesting place. Its most notable feature is the fantastically deformed cypresses that writhe in the wind on the black cliffs above the ocean. Stevenson once lived in the town, towards the end of the last century, and afterwards wrote nostalgically of it: "The woods and the Pacific rule between them the climate of this seaboard region. On the streets of Monterey, when the air does not smell salt from the one, it will be blowing perfumed from the resinous treetops of the other."

Steinbeck became acquainted early in life with the paisanos he was to write of in *Tortilla Flat*. In the Modern Library reprint of that book he tells in the foreword of a paisano boy he went to school with in Salinas: "We called him the *piojo*, and he was a nice, kind, brown little boy. He had no mother or father—only an elder sister whom we loved and admired. We called her, with a great deal of respect, a hoor-lady. She had the reddest cheeks in town, and she made tomato sandwiches for us sometimes. Now in the little house where the *piojo* and his sister the hoor-lady lived, the faucet at the sink was broken off. A wooden plug had been pounded into the pipe to keep it from leaking. The water for cooking and drinking was drawn from the toilet. There was a tin dipper on the floor to get it out. When the water was low, you simply flushed the toilet and there was a new supply. No one was allowed to use this toilet as a toilet.

Once when we sequestered a colony of pollywogs in the bowl, the hoor-lady gave us hell and then flushed them down the sewer." Steinbeck cannot in later life find that this is "shocking" or anything like it: "I have been subjected to decency for a long time, and I still can't think of the hoor-lady as (that nastiest of words) a prostitute, nor of *piojo's* many *uncles*, those jolly men who sometimes gave us nickels, as her clients."

During his high school years, Steinbeck from time to time worked around ranches. He was graduated from Salinas high school in 1918, and for a while was employed as a chemist at the beet-sugar factory near the town. In the autumn of 1919 he entered Stanford University, at Palo Alto. He made none of the athletic teams while he was there, though at first he tried out "vaguely" for crew and football. In the spring of 1920 he left Stanford for a while, returning in the autumn but disappearing again soon afterwards. He went to work on a ranch at King City, which is about halfway between Jolon and Soledad, the respective settings of *To A God Unknown* and *Of Mice and Men*. Steinbeck had sometimes visited Jolon in childhood; it was a settlement lying just outside the Salinas Valley, and it retained something of its old Spanish flavor—the San Antonio de Padua Mission nearby was fairly well preserved, though it had been severely shaken in the 1906 earthquake. King City was eighteen miles north, on the Salinas River, which sent a branch, the San Antonio, out past Jolon. Soledad was another eighteen miles above King City on the Salinas: Soledad also had an old mission, but a hopelessly shattered one. The place where Steinbeck was working and the varied jobs that came his way at that ranch were helping him both to absorb background material and to know at first hand what it was like to be an agricultural laborer. He has always been sympathetic to the common man and his problems, and unlike so many writers he is never bored with simple, illiterate people. When asked, after the publication of *In Dubious Battle,* if he had swung to the left, he answered that he had always essentially been on the left.

Steinbeck had argued about socialism with the ranch workers. He had some hopes for socialism in those days, but feared that stupidity and greed would keep it from being fully successful. Back in Salinas after working near King City, in the spring of 1921 he was evolving a theory of "Partial Immortality of the Mind," which threw out the concept of soul and yet attempted to answer the questions of spiritualism and religion. He argued about this with some local ministers, who spread reports that young Steinbeck was off-center. This irritated him. He felt he was meant to be a writer, and was sending manuscripts to eastern magazines and collecting rejection slips. Because most of the other boys of his generation were interested only in chasing girls, Steinbeck used to ask rhetorically if this were an age of weak minds.

Steinbeck returned to Stanford for the academic years 1922-23. He roomed at this time with C. A. Sheffield, who afterwards taught English at Stanford and later became a newspaperman in northern California. Steinbeck didn't stay on regularly at Stanford, but dropped out again, worked on other ranches and spent a summer as night chemist at the sugar-beet factory where he had been employed before. For a while he helped to build the first road below Big Sur, where there had previously been only steep bridle paths and mule tracks. The place appealed to his imagination: he has said one feels distinctly "that people lived there long, long ago, and have left their presence."

77

Steinbeck left Stanford for good in 1925. He had announced that he wasn't studying for a degree, and had roamed over the curriculum at will, taking whatever subjects he pleased. In the several years he spent at Stanford he earned only about half of the required 180 units. He wrote both poetry and prose for the university magazines, the *Spectator* and the *Lit*. It was at this time that he put on paper the first version of what was to become his first published novel, *Cup of Gold*; it was then a short story called "A Lady in Infra-Red." He took all the writing courses in school except one, a course in playwriting for which the professor considered him unfit.

His ambition to be a writer led him to New York after he left Stanford for the last time. He worked for a newspaper for a short while after his arrival in New York: he was pitched out of this job for reporting the news philosophically and poetically instead of presenting the blunt facts. He became a hod carrier and in this capacity helped build the new Madison Square Garden. When the Garden was finished, he stayed in New York trying to become a free-lance writer. Guy Holt, who was then an editor for McBride and Company, had encouraged Steinbeck to prepare a book of short stories. But after Holt had left McBride to join the John Day Company, the new McBride editor wouldn't accept the stories despite the brouhaha Steinbeck raised in the office. Later Steinbeck collapsed on the street and was taken to a hospital. He decided it was time to return to California.

Steinbeck liked, and still likes, to travel between California and New York on a freight boat. Now he is a passenger; in those days he was a deck hand. As a member of the crew he used to join in the crap-shooting and the general story telling. He also used to be called upon when his shipmates wanted someone to write letters to their girls. Some of those sailors have kept in touch with him, and he still gets illiterate scrawls from them.

A stopover on the Isthmus of Panama had provided Steinbeck with some of the backgi und material for his contemplated novel, *Cup of Gold*. He wrote and rewrote this during the copious leisure time permitted by his next job: he became caretaker of an estate at Lake Tahoe, high in the Sierras on the Nevada border. He later worked at a nearby fish hatchery. He has said that the solitude of those two mountain winters refined all the malice out of his system.

McBride and Company accepted *Cup of Gold*, which was actually the fourth novel he had written. It was published in August 1929, and while it was not a money-maker, Steinbeck felt sufficiently encouraged to get married. His bride was Carol Henning who, like his mother, had come from San Jose. She ran away with him and they were married in Los Angeles in 1930.

Steinbeck and his wife went to live in a small house his father gave them in Pacific Grove. Although it is near the art colony at Carmel-by-the-Sea, and although it lies just below Monterey, Pacific Grove has none of Carmel's Bohemianism or of Monterey's lurid reputation. *Tortilla Flat* contains a biting reference to the town: "In the neighboring and Methodist village of Pacific Grove the W.C.T.U. met for tea and discussion, listened while a little lady described the vice and prostitution of Monterey with energy and color. She thought a committee should visit these resorts to see exactly how terrible conditions really were. They had gone over the situation so often, and they needed new facts." Yet Steinbeck frequently said he liked Pacific Grove. Once he admitted that the little town was a hard one to get out of: there was "a strong pull" in Pacific Grove.

His second book, The Pastures of Heaven, came out in the autumn of 1932, and has a curious history. It had originally been accepted by the firm of Brewer, Warren and Putnam. This company went out of business at the moment of publishing the book. But it had aroused the enthusiasm of a member of the firm, Robert O. Ballou, who then brought the novel out on his own. There is a bibliographical confusion about the first edition of The Pastures of Heaven, which bears several imprints. Of the first 2500 sheets, 1650 were published with the Brewer, Warren and Putnam title-page and binding. This is of course the legitimate first issue. Ballou took over the remaining 850 sets of unbound sheets, and this is where the confusion begins. Authorities differ as to whether these sheets were used for three more issues, making four altogether, or merely two more, making three in all. Ben Abramson, one Steinbeck authority, counts as second issue whatever copies appeared with Brewer, Warren and Putnam on the spine and a Robert O. Ballou title-page pasted in on the stub of the original. Another authority, the assiduous Steinbeck collector Lawrence Clark Powell (whose check lists have appeared in the Publishers' Weekly, the Book Collector's Packet and the Colophon), has never seen one of these copies of mixed insignia, and calls them "merely freaks or strays, not entitled to ranking as separate issues."* Powell holds that the second issue is the one with the Ballou binding and tipped-in title page, which Abramson calls the third issue. Ballou didn't have all the 850 sets of sheets rebound, so when Covici-Friede took over Steinbeck's work in 1935, they used the balance of them, providing their own binding and tipping in their own title-page.

*Abramson asserts that he has handled many of these.

This may serve as either the third or fourth issue, as you prefer. One thing is certain: the man in all the world who cares least about the question is John Steinbeck.

Ballou also published Steinbeck's next book, *To A God Unknown*, which came out in the fall of 1933. *The Pastures of Heaven* had lost money, and Ballou was having a hard time to keep afloat. But he was buoyed up by the interest other publishers had shown in Steinbeck's work: Simon and Schuster, the Viking Press, Morrow and Company and Harcourt, Brace and Company were watching Steinbeck eagerly. But the money Ballou had been able to raise to keep on publishing Steinbeck was lost on *To A God Unknown*, and Ballou went under. If he had weathered the failure of that novel, he might be a publisher still.

Steinbeck was not having an easy time during these years. None of the magazines was responsive to his short stories with the exception of the *North American Review*, a once powerful journal which at that time had lapsed into a respectable obscurity. The *North American Review* published the first two parts of *The Red Pony* in November and December 1933, "The Murder" in April 1934, "The Raid" in October 1934, and "The White Quail" in March 1935. The editors of no other magazines were enterprising enough to go after Steinbeck, although "The Murder" had been reprinted in the 1934 edition of the *O. Henry Memorial Award Stories*. It is amusing to note that a certain showy best-selling magazine noted for its hunt after names rather than quality turned down a Steinbeck story but had to swallow this same story when Steinbeck's agents were approached for material after its author himself became a name. The sequel is no less amusing: the story was the leading feature of the issue in which it appeared.

81

The Pastures of Heaven had been published in London in 1933 by Philip Allan and Company, Ltd. It was still not a money-maker, though it received friendly notices in the press. This didn't increase Steinbeck's respect for the British, but it deepened his contempt of American reviewers. He and his wife were in almost desperate straits, and he was wondering if he would have to become a ranch worker again to earn a living. His wife had a job for a while with the local Chamber of Commerce. The Steinbecks were lucky enough to own a small boat which they could use for fishing on Monterey Bay: they were living on twenty-five dollars a month, and fish comprised the bulk of their diet.

Steinbeck's novels were even less appreciated in the Methodist center of Pacific Grove than they were elsewhere. In 1934 a committee of citizens demanded that his books be removed from the shelves of the Pacific Grove library. In New York, the interest which several publishers had shown in Steinbeck's work had sunk with the failure of *To A God Unknown*. Nine firms turned down his next novel, *Tortilla Flat*, a collection of stories and legends he had been gathering among his friends the Monterey *paisanos* and in other parts of the town.

Then there was an upturn in Steinbeck's fortunes, due to the enthusiasm which Ben Abramson, the Chicago bookseller, felt for the work of this unsuccessful but promising author. Abramson had been buying up old copies of Steinbeck and had been telling his customers that this was the coming author, the man to collect. One day the publisher Pascal Covici was visiting Chicago and while at the Argus Book Shop he heard Abramson chanting praises of Steinbeck. It was a name unknown to him. Abramson pressed Steinbeck's last two books upon him, and Covici agreed that they were promising. As soon as he arrived back in New York he 'phoned Steinbeck's agents, who passed on the worn manuscript of *Tortilla Flat* to one more publisher. But this one accepted at once, and from then on life was different for Steinbeck. All this hinged upon one little incident: authors are often helped to success by booksellers who infuse their customers with eagerness for books already published, but it is not often that a bookseller works so directly on behalf of an unfriended manuscript as Abramson did in this instance.

When *Tortilla Flat* came out in May 1935 it was warmly greeted by reviewers and had a good sale. Seven printings were necessary in less than a year. Paramount Studios bought the film rights, but the picture has not yet been made: the actor George Raft refused to play Danny, a role he considered beneath his dignity.

Tortilla Flat shocked some Californians and made others believe that they had a valuable possession in such picturesque "natives." The book was awarded the annual Gold Medal of the Commonwealth Club of California. The sales of *Tortilla Flat* were bringing in enough money to enable Steinbeck to paint his house and refinish the walls and floors and ceilings. *To A God Unknown* had been published in England by William Heinemann, Ltd., in the spring of 1935, but the British critics were not very pleased with it—the *Times* was savage because the jacket blurb compared the book with the work of D. H. Lawrence—and it fared no better than it had in America.

Steinbeck refused to consider working on the screen-play of *Tortilla Flat*. He and his wife had been planning for some time to visit Mexico, and now for the first time they had enough money to go. In July 1935 he signed a contract with Covici-Friede for six books. Steinbeck might have driven a harder bargain than he did drive with Covici-Friede, but he liked the firm and was satisfied with the terms he received. He had completed *In Dubious Battle*, but its publication was delayed because one of Covici's readers had suggested to Steinbeck that Mac be drawn closer to the communist party-line; Steinbeck sent the manuscript to another publisher, and Covici heard of this just in time to retrieve it — he published it as written, but not until the next year; meanwhile, he was bringing out new issues of *The Pastures of Heaven* and *To A God Unknown*, while in association with him George J. McLeod, Ltd., of Toronto, was beginning to publish Steinbeck in Canada.

In the autumn the Steinbecks at last went to Mexico, in their old car. They had intended to stay through the winter, seeing fiestas at Oaxaca, Guadalupe and other places, but Steinbeck felt he couldn't work in Mexico. It was so different, like being in an undersea world: the Mexicans seemed to live at a deep dream-level. The Steinbecks came back to California before the year was out. Steinbeck felt Mexico was far too bewildering to write anything about, at least from what he knew of it so far.

In Dubious Battle appeared in February 1936, and while it didn't have the wide sale of *Tortilla Flat*, it increased Steinbeck's prestige as an author. This book was also awarded the annual gold medal of the Commonwealth Club. Steinbeck declined to go to the banquet to receive this; his refusal was merely a matter of shyness.

In the summer of 1936 Steinbeck moved away from Pacific Grove, where the coastal fogs had begun to make his wife miserable with sinus. They left their little vine-clad cottage and moved to the Santa Cruz Mountains near Los Gatos, where they had a home built along the lines of an old-fashioned California ranch house. There are 'coons and 'possums and rabbits all about, and at night the coyotes can be heard howling. The house is set in an oak forest, and has a long veranda overlooking the Santa Clara valley, in the heart of which Steinbeck's mother and his wife had been born.

The producer Herman Shumlin had an idea that *In Dubious Battle* would make an excellent play. He wanted John O'Hara, author of the novels *Appointment at Samarra* and *Butterfield 8*, to dramatize Steinbeck's book, but O'Hara was busily writing film scripts in Hollywood. Shumlin then tried to induce Steinbeck to make a play out of *In Dubious Battle*, but Steinbeck was reluctant. He felt that book was already a piece of the past: times were so wild, conditions were changing so rapidly—and Steinbeck felt that he was growing. He had been working on a small experimental novel, *Of Mice and Men*, and wanted to get at the big theme that was gestating in him: it would have something in common with *In Dubious Battle* but would be smoother, more moving, more expansive. His interest in the migrant laborers was brought to a high pitch by his experiences in gathering material for a *Nation* article, "Dubious Battle in California" (published in the September 12, 1936 issue) and for the series of sketches he wrote for the *San Francisco News* (published in October 1936). These last were re-issued in pamphlet form in 1938, with an epilogue, by the Simon J. Lubin Society of San Francisco. It was just after completing *Of Mice and Men* that Steinbeck had gone out once again to see the squatters' camps and talk to the men working in the fields. He felt that California was not far from civil war.

The manuscript of the novel-version of *Of Mice and Men* was submitted to Shumlin as a possible play but he rejected it. Covici enthusiastically published it as a novel in February 1937. Steinbeck's dog Toby had chewed up the manuscript, but not until after type had been set and proofs corrected. *Of Mice and Men* was selected as a Book-of-the-Month Club choice. Covici had telegraphed Steinbeck about this but didn't hear anything in response for two weeks, when a penny postcard came from Los Gatos asking, "What does it mean?" It meant that 75,000 copies had been sold in a lump, and a greater general interest than might have been expected had been aroused in advance. *Of Mice and Men* became a best-seller.

That summer Steinbeck went traveling. He and his wife left San Francisco on a freighter that took them, via the Panama Canal, to Philadelphia. There they quietly got aboard a train for New York. It was the night of a dinner for Thomas Mann, and Covici prevailed upon the Steinbecks to go. But Steinbeck had nothing to wear except the blue linen slacks, sneakers and sweater he had on at the moment. Someone in Covici's office lent him a dark blue suit, and no one in the Covici party dressed formally that night. It was Steinbeck's first banquet, and he found himself unable to swallow the speeches. He stole away to the hotel bar, where he said mournfully over a brandy and soda that it was a pity for a writer like Thomas Mann to have to give and receive such hollow talk.

Covici had a hard time persuading Steinbeck to meet reporters during that brief New York visit. But at last, fortified with a bottle of brandy, Steinbeck consented to see them in the publisher's office. After all, he had once been a reporter himself, even if his career was one of the shortest in the history of journalism. California has produced some extremely picturesque writers, such as Jack London, and has helped to mould others equally picturesque, such as Joaquin Miller, and while reporters found that this blue-eyed sandy-haired six footer who faced them across the bar of a publisher's desk was quiet and less spectacular than some of his predecessors, they also found that he was good copy. The photographers had a big day getting pictures of Steinbeck sitting there with the bottle looming so large beside him.

None of the reporters who interviewed Steinbeck seems to have made the comparison, but perhaps his personality was more like that of a Nexoe or a Gorky than the typical swashing writer come out of the American west, just as his books—despite their indelible American stamp—often seem to have more in common atmospherically and in attitude with the work of continental European authors than they do with the writings of his fellow-countrymen. A man like Steinbeck presents a difficult combination to find the key to, with his bourgeois-childhood background, his discernible cultivation, and his proletarian sympathies. He can not only write strong yet delicate prose, but he can also go to any sun-blazed California ranch and win the admiration of the workers bucking grain in the fields.

Steinbeck as usual guarded himself and tried to keep the talk impersonal that afternoon when the reporters swarmed around him in Covici's office. He is a facile enough talker among people he knows well, but he measured his words that day. When the conversation was forced back upon him he said a few things about his work, mostly discussing *Of Mice and Men*, which was to be produced in the fall. It had already been staged directly from the novel by a labor theater group in San Francisco, and Steinbeck had learned a bit from that. But he told the newspapermen he wanted to cut out the between-act intermissions entirely: these were "for clacking women."

The Steinbecks went to Europe on a freighter in the middle of May 1937. They went to Londonderry to visit some of his mother's relatives, they bicycled through the Scandinavian countries, and they looked in on Russia. They were gone three months altogether. Steinbeck found Russia as bewildering in one way as Mexico had been in another, and said he was not sure what he had come out with. He had made his visit during the confused time of the party purges.

Upon returning to the United States, the Steinbecks went to George S. Kaufman's farm near Doylestown, Pennsylvania, where Steinbeck wrote the final version of the play. Kaufman was to direct it for Sam H. Harris. The Steinbecks took a train to Detroit in early autumn, not waiting to see the play produced. They bought an automobile in Detroit and drove west, visiting Chicago for a few days. On their way to the Coast they stopped in Oklahoma, where Steinbeck gathered material for The Grapes of Wrath. He joined the hordes of migratory workers drifting west, lived in their crude camps, and worked in the fields with them when they reached the California agricultural country. Then he went back to his ranch at Los Gatos to put his experiences in the book (at different times announced as Oklahoma and Lettuceville) that was to become The Grapes of Wrath.

Of Mice and Men had its Broadway opening on November 23, 1937. That afternoon Steinbeck and his wife drove ten miles to the ranch of a friend who had a telephone. They arrived at 5:30 p.m., just as the play was about to begin (at 8:30 New York time). Covici gave a long-distance report of the first-night audience's responses at the end of each act. Steinbeck lost the wager

he made with Covici—a barrel of California muscatel—
that the play wouldn't last a week on Broadway. It was
one of the hits of the season, and was given the award
of the Drama Critics' Circle for being what the New
York reviewers considered the best play of the year.

Steinbeck had earned one of the important American
literary reputations of the century, but he had not yet
become popular in England (where William Heinemann, Ltd., has continued to publish his full-length
books). He has been exuberantly praised by such dif-
ferently influential critics as Humbert Wolfe, James
Agate and Herbert Read, but none of his books has yet
been a British best-seller.* Steinbeck has found appre-
ciative readers in Sweden, however, where some of his
work has appeared in translation, and South America has
demonstrated its interest in the form of a study by Mau-
rice Coindreau, "John Steinbeck, *novelista de California*," which appeared in Buenos Aires in 1938 (*Sur,
Revista mensual*, Ano 8, pp. 7-19).

Tortilla Flat didn't repeat the stage success that *Of
Mice and Men* had. *Tortilla Flat* was dramatized by
Jack Kirkland, who had adapted *Tobacco Road*, and was
put on Broadway not long after *Of Mice and Men*
opened. The critics were bitter about the play-version of
Tortilla Flat, which was considered vulgar, and Kirkland
didn't help the fortunes of the production when he
tried, in the Whistler tradition, to beat up one of the
critics in a cafe. Whistler at least had a cane for attack
and defense: Kirkland, who had only himself, was
pitched out onto the pavement. Covici-Friede had ar-

*When a critic in *Time and Tide* spoke of the perfection of a book
he called "Men and Mice, by Steinbock," a Heinemann official
wrote the editor to inquire whether the young man hadn't meant
"Moce and Min, by Beckstein."

ranged to publish the dramatization of *Tortilla Flat*, but cancelled plans to do so when the play closed after five performances.

Steinbeck worked steadily at *The Grapes of Wrath* after his return to Los Gatos. Meanwhile, his publisher was going out of business. Covici-Friede had barely got through the depression; although the firm kept its double name, Donald Friede had broken away in 1936 and gone to Hollywood to be an agent; Covici had a Kohinoor in Steinbeck, and he tried to hold his creditors off for a while longer, but they moved in during the summer of 1938 and took over the property. Some of the other New York publishers had a fierce battle over the Steinbeck contract, which Covici kept tightly clutched to him. When the smoke cleared away, Covici was a member of the staff at Viking Press, and in September that company brought out the first collection of Steinbeck's short stories, *The Long Valley*. Steinbeck had some $6,000 due for back royalties; it was estimated that his books — principally *Of Mice and Men* — had brought him about $50,000 by that time. The Viking Press issued *The Grapes of Wrath* in April 1939, and plans to publish Steinbeck's future work.

The completion of *The Grapes of Wrath* at the end of 1938 left Steinbeck nervously exhausted. He was confined to bed for some weeks, and forbidden by doctor's orders to read or write. It was the end of the second lustre of his career as a writer, and it may be the end of his second literary period. Perhaps his writing will now take another direction. It is of course impossible to make a definite prediction at this time.

Steinbeck loathes biographical sketches. He once wrote, in answer to a query that had been sent him while he was still an obscure author, "I really like the biographical method used by my dictionary. It would say, John Steinbeck, writer, born 1902, died (?) There is method. There is finish. There is even suspense." He believes an author should be known purely by his work, and he has tried to keep himself out of his own as much as possible. He applies this theory to others as well as to himself. His disillusionment with Thomas Mann has already been mentioned. He once refused to meet his fellow-Californian, Robinson Jeffers, who has also written so much about Monterey County, "because his poetry is perfect to me, and I don't think one should get the man mixed up with the work." Sometimes Steinbeck views these matters with tongue in cheek, as in the case of the questionnaire he filled out for the California state librarian, which Lawrence Clark Powell rescued after it was ejected from the files where it had lain for some time in all its innocence:

Name: John Ernst Alcibiades Socrates Steinbeck.
Born: Lesbos, Magna Graece, 1902.
Father: Heredotus Xenephon Steinbeck.
Mother: Chloe Mathilde Lopez.
Married to: Jo Alfreda Jones, in Tia Juana.
Writings: The Unstrung Harpie. Donahoe, 1906.
            Taxgiversating Tehabedrous. MacDougall, 1927.
            Barnacles. (Ballinadae.) Monograph. 2 vols. Stanford University Press.
            Bugs, a Critical Study. Morbide Press.

Steinbeck's musical interests have been mentioned at the appropriate points in the separate study of his books, where it was explained that before he began writing he often played the music of such composers as Dvorak, Brahms and Handel, drawing his mood from them and sometimes constructing his work after symphonic patterns. It has been said that his taste for classical music in no way inhibits his appreciation of a well-sung torch song.

In literature he distrusts most of the moderns. He was a devotee of Cabell and Donn Byrne in his college days but he violently repudiated them later, while the controlled enthusiasm he once felt for Sherwood Anderson, Norman Douglas, Carl Van Vechten and other guides of youth in the 1920's has long since faded. He partly admires Hemingway and D. H. Lawrence, and likes Willa Cather immensely. Although he is cagey about most contemporary novels and reads as few of them as possible, he was strongly moved by John Hargrave's *Summer Time Ends* when it came out in 1936. Steinbeck has expressed his disgust of Proust, who "wrote his sickness, and I don't like sick writing."

Literary references in Steinbeck's novels include some interesting items. In *Cup of Gold* most of them appear as books read in the library of James Flower by the young Henry Morgan, who was for a time a privileged slave on Flower's plantation in the West Indies. There are references to Scot's *Discoverie of Witchcraft*; the "system of Descartes"; the "new-found school of Bacon"; *The Effects of Alcoholic Spirits, Momentary and Perpetual*; Caesar's *Commentaries*; the "shrewd elder Cato"; "Holmaron on the Inquisition"; Xenephon. Perhaps the sixteenth and seventeenth century items had been read by Steinbeck in preparing his background—or they may have been taken from bibliographical notes. John Evelyn appears as a character.

The Pastures of Heaven has even more literary references. Miss Morgan, the school teacher, reads novels to her pupils, novels by Scott, Zane Grey, James Oliver Curwood and Jack London. This seems like good ob-

92

servation on Steinbeck's part; these are just the books a
school teacher in a small California community would
read to the children. Junius Maltby is a different matter.
His reading list may have been taken from life, but on
the other hand it is more likely to be what Steinbeck
imagined it would have been: Maltby's favorite reading
was Stevenson's *Travels with a Donkey*, and he is mentioned as reading "the Gallic wars" to the boys of the
valley. He also read them the *Treasure Island* of his
admired Stevenson, whose *Kidnapped* he generally carried around in his pocket. Another author Junius liked
was David Grayson, whose *Adventures in Contentment*
often pleased him: if Steinbeck was making out a reading list for an idealized character, perhaps this item
causes him a faint embarrassment now. But the volumes
mentioned as being read by Richard and John Whiteside wouldn't make him blush today—Herodotus, Xenephon, Thucydides, Virgil. Steinbeck regularly reads and
re-reads these authors and others among the ancients.

To *A God Unknown* has a Vedic hymn quoted at the
front of the book. Elizabeth McGreggor, whom Joseph
married, had been a school teacher, daughter of a
Marxian (or neo-Marxian) harness-maker. Elizabeth
"had read excerpts from Plato and Lucretius, knew several titles of Aeschylus, Aristophanes and Euripides, and
had a classical background resting on Homer and Virgil."
When Joseph came courting, she tried to discuss Homer
with him; later she told him she was reading *Pippa
Passes* and asked him if he liked Robert Browning.
("Have you decided yet? . . . I must ask you that first.
I don't know who Browning is.") Father Angelo appro-
priately read *La Vida del San Bartelomeo*.

The only literary reference in *Tortilla Flat* is a general
one the author makes to Arthur and Roland and Robin

93

Hood. *In Dubious Battle* would probably be free from such references but for the list of books Jim, the communist recruit, mentioned as having read after a man he met "in the park" began to guide his reading: "He made lists like Plato's *Republic*, and the *Utopia*, and Bellamy, and like Herodotus and Gibbon and Macaulay and Carlyle and Prescott, and like Spinoza and Hegel and Kant and Nietzsche and Schopenhauer. He even made me read *Das Kapital*." The nearest thing to a literary reference to be found in *Of Mice and Men* is the mention of a western story magazine. Steinbeck was writing about downright illiterate people then, as he was in *The Grapes of Wrath*, which also mentions a western story magazine but in addition has unexpected references to *Pilgrim's Progress* and to Harold Bell Wright's *The Winning of Barbara Worth*. The Bunyan book is mentioned by an anonymous voice among the wandering people in *The Grapes of Wrath*, while one of the main characters of that novel, Tom Joad, says "I never could keep Scripture straight sence I read a book name' *The Winning of Barbara Worth*."

The bulk of Steinbeck's reading among current books is scientific, economic and sociological. He has read closely the books Jim Nolan of *In Dubious Battle* mentioned, and we have seen how his reading among the classics resembles that of the Whitesides in *The Pastures of Heaven*. Steinbeck has also been deeply moved by Dostoyevsky and Tolstoy. When very young he read *Crime and Punishment*, *Madame Bovary*, *Paradise Lost*, George Eliot's novels and *The Return of the Native*—he says now he remembers these not as books but as things that happened to him.

Because of the mystic strain that persists in Steinbeck despite all his realism, it is not always easy to distinguish between the abstract and the concrete in his allusions to his childhood. He has spoken of wanting to write a child's book someday that will have nothing in it of giants and fairies but will present that realer, sharper, more brightly-colored world than adults know. When he tells of being a child and looking into a vacant lot across the street from his house and seeing a full-maned African lion there, it is hard to understand whether this was an actual lion escaped from some circus or whether Steinbeck was having an experience similar (though far homelier) to those Blake knew as a child when he saw God put his forehead to the window, when he passed a tree full of radiant angels at Peckham Rye, and when he found Ezekiel sitting in a field one summer day. An American boy with a visionary Celtic strain might easily see a circus lion across the street.

Steinbeck hasn't lost this visionary sense. Today he speaks of his dog Toby as seeing presences that are invisible to others. And John Steinbeck feels that even his new ranch house is thronged with spirits out of his own hereditary past, vertical Prussians and equally stubborn and rigid Irish. It was intimated in the critical section of this book that Steinbeck might one day turn back to mystic writing, but of a sounder and more disciplined kind.

It is difficult to prophesy anything about Steinbeck; his oldest friends confess they find him baffling. One thing is certain, and that is that success has not spoiled him. (He prefers to wear his oldest clothes, and he and his wife still roll their own cigarettes.) He resents the accidents of fame: his mail is full of demands — not requests, but demands. While he was working on *The Grapes of Wrath* he carelessly gave a reporter some information about the setting and the characters of the book:

95

the reporter wrote a long and garbled account of this in the paper, making up his own story, and for two agonizing months Steinbeck felt the book had gone sour on him.

He doesn't enjoy being a best-seller; the fact that he is one causes him to doubt his work, and to wonder if it is lacking in ideas, since it attracts so many readers. He said at one time that he would prefer to have a steady group of about 20,000 readers; then he could make a comfortable living without being a front-page figure. Another time, in speaking of the ten dollar limited edition of *The Red Pony*, he said he favored twenty-five cent books and unlimited editions.

He thinks it is mathematically predictable that the crowd will one day turn on him. This is not too unlikely, considering the fickleness of the American public. Steinbeck has a long career ahead of him. It is impossible, at the time this is being written, to gauge the public response to *The Grapes of Wrath*, but it is safe to predict—and not solely on the basis of the tremendous advance sale— that *The Grapes of Wrath* will be a long-term best-seller. This despite the fact that almost every passage in the book would ordinarily be considered violently revolutionary and profane by the majority of those who will read it. But the author of *Of Mice and Men* is in vogue now: in America, those in vogue can do little wrong. The vogue will last as long as Steinbeck can hold the public's interest; eventually he may be displaced by writers whom the public will consider moré interesting, but such a day seems, at this time, very remote.

BIBLIOGRAPHICAL CHECK-LIST OF

FIRST EDITIONS

(This does not attempt to be a complete bibliography, but it is a check-list of first editions as far as can be determined at this time. It notes every "first" appearance of an item by Steinbeck between the covers of a book. Steinbeck's magazine appearances and collations of critical items concerning him will have to be left to some future compiler of a specialized Steinbeck bibliography.)

CUP OF GOLD: *A Life of Henry Morgan, Buccaneer, With Occasional Reference to History.* New York, Robert M. McBride & Co. 1929. First Published, August, 1929, appears on the verso of the title page. Covici-Friede issued a new edition in 1936, made from photo-offset plates of the McBride edition, with a foreword by Lewis Gannett.

THE PASTURES OF HEAVEN. New York, Brewer, Warren & Putnam. 1932. There are four issues of this book. In all, approximately 2500 sets of sheets comprise the first edition. The first issue, consisting of about 650 copies, has Brewer, Warren & Putnam on the title page and spine. The second issue consists of copies with the Brewer, Warren & Putnam title page, but with Robert Ballou stamped on the spine. 1000 copies of this issue were available. The third issue has a new title page tipped in, with the name Robert O. Ballou as publisher, and

Robert Ballou stamped on the spine. The fourth issue has a title page tipped in, with the name Covici-Friede as publisher, and is so stamped on the spine.

TO A GOD UNKNOWN. New York, Robert O. Ballou. [1933]. First published 1933 appears on the verso of the title page. The entire edition consists of approximately 1500 sets of sheets. Of these, 600 comprise the first issue, having the Ballou imprint. In 1935, the remaining copies were issued with Covici-Friede title page tipped in on a stub, and the name Covici-Friede stamped on the spine. Copies having the Covici imprint constitute the second issue.

O. HENRY MEMORIAL AWARD. PRIZE STORIES OF 1934. *Edited by* HARRY HANSEN. Garden City, Doubleday Doran & Co., Inc. 1934. Contains the story *The Murder* by Steinbeck, reprinted from THE NORTH AMERICAN REVIEW. This story was later included in *The Long Valley*.

TORTILLA FLAT. New York, Covici-Friede. [1935]. First Edition not indicated, but later printings noted on the verso of the title page. Illustrated by Ruth Gannett. An advance issue of 500 copies, bound in wrappers, was issued for promotional purposes. Reprinted in the Modern Library series, 1937, with a foreword written expressly for it by the author.

IN DUBIOUS BATTLE. New York, Covici-Friede. [1936]. First Edition not indicated, but later printings noted on the verso of the title page. A deluxe edition of 99 copies, numbered and signed by the author, and boxed, was also issued.

NOTHING SO MONSTROUS: A Story. [New York, The Pynson Printers]. 1936. The Junius Maltby episode from *The Pastures of Heaven*, reprinted, with an epilogue written for this edition by the author. Illustrated by Donald McKay. Limited to 370 copies, unnumbered.

SAINT KATY THE VIRGIN. [New York, Covici-Friede. 1936]. Deluxe edition only, limited to 199 copies, numbered and signed by the author. Later included in *The Long Valley*.

OF MICE AND MEN. New York, Covici-Friede. [1937]. The first printing consists of 2500 copies. On page 9, lines 2 and 3, reading upwards, read "and only moved because the heavy hands were/pendula." There is a dot between the two numbers 8 on page 88. The top is stained blue. The second and subsequent printings have the errors corrected, and green stained top. The first illustrated edition, issued (in London) by William Heinemann, Ltd., later in 1937, decorated by Michael Rothenstein.

THE RED PONY: I. THE GIFT, II. THE GREAT MOUNTAINS, III. THE PROMISE. New York, Covici-Friede. 1937. Deluxe edition only, limited to 699 copies, numbered and signed by the author. Later included in *The Long Valley*.

OF MICE AND MEN: *A Play in Three Acts.* New York, Covici-Friede. [1937].

DEL MONTE RECIPES. Del Monte, [California]. 1937. Issued by the Del Monte Properties Company as a promotion piece for the Hotel Del Monte. Steinbeck contributed a recipe to this collection of favorite recipes of famous persons.

THEIR BLOOD IS STRONG. San Francisco, The Simon J. Lubin Society of California, Inc. 1938. A pamphlet. Published April, 1938, appears on the title page of the first printing. Subsequent issues are so noted. This is a reprint of seven articles on California Migratory Labor conditions which Steinbeck wrote for the San Francisco News in 1936, with a 1938 Epilogue.

THE BEST SHORT STORIES, 1938, edited by EDWARD J. O'BRIEN. Boston, Houghton Mifflin Co. 1938. First edition must have date on title page. Contains the story Crysanthemum. Later included in The Long Valley.

THE LONG VALLEY. New York, The Viking Press. 1938. First published in September 1938 noted on the verse of the title page. Two stories, Flight and The Leader of the People, had never before been printed.

O. HENRY MEMORIAL AWARD. PRIZE STORIES OF 1938. Edited by HARRY HANSEN. New York, Doubleday Doran & Co., Inc. 1938. First Edition printed on verso of the title page. Contains the story The Promise by Steinbeck, reprinted from HARPERS.

GRAPES OF WRATH. New York, The Viking Press. [1939]. First published in April 1939 noted on verso of title page. ———

MORGAN SAILS THE CARIBBEAN, by BERTON BRALEY. New York, The Macmillan Co. 1934. A letter from Steinbeck to the author, giving him permission to use certain incidents from *Cup of Gold* is printed, for the first time, in the acknowledgment.

THE COLOPHON: *New Series.* New York [Pynson Printers, Inc.]. 1938. The Autumn number, Volume 3, Number 4, contains an article by Lawrence Clark Powell entitled *Toward A Bibliography of John Steinbeck*, in which a brief travesty autobiography from State Librarians' Questionnaire is printed for the first time.

NOTE

Cup of Gold, To A God Unknown, Tortilla Flat, In Dubious Battle, Of Mice and Men and *The Long Valley* were published in England by William Heinemann, Ltd., of London, who made their own plates for each issue, and in Canada by George J. McLeod, Ltd., of Toronto, who imported complete bound copies from Covici-Friede and the Viking Press. McLeod also published *The Pastures of Heaven* and *The Red Pony* under this arrangement. Philip Allan and Company, Ltd., published *The Pastures of Heaven* in London. *The Grapes of Wrath* is being published in London by William Heinemann, Ltd., and in Toronto by the Macmillan Company of Canada, Ltd.

A NOTE CONCERNING THE MAP

THE MAP of the "Steinbeck Country" included in this volume is intended to be only a guide, in a general sort of way, to readers of Steinbeck's novels and to those interested in tracing the relationship between his life and his work. There is no exact parallel between some of these places as they exist, and as they are imaginatively reflected in his stories. Steinbeck writes, "I have usually avoided using actual places to avoid hurting feelings for, although I rarely use a person or a story as it is — neighbors love only too well to attribute them to someone. Thus you will find that the Pastures of Heaven does not look very much like Corral de Tierra, you'll find no pine forests in Jolon and as for the valley in *In Dubious Battle* — it is a composite valley as it is a composite strike. If it has the characteristics of Pajaro nevertheless there was no strike there. If it is like the cotton strike, that wasn't apples. Only in this new book* have I turned to actual places — that and *Tortilla Flat*. For I still feel it useless and foolish to hurt individual feelings . . . the maps don't work because I mixed up the topography on purpose."

We have prepared the map in this spirit: it is merely meant to indicate where certain imaginatively conceived people lived, and even if the settings are in some cases "mixed," we tried to show the locale that is essentially suggested in each story. Most writers have scrambled their settings in this way. But there is usually a prevailing atmosphere, and it is this we have considered in each case where there might be confusion. Passages in the critical and biographical sections of the present volume will doubtless suggest reasons for the choices made in certain instances on this map.

* The Grapes of Wrath